Number sequences

A sequence is usually a list of **numbers in a pattern**.

Look at the difference between each number to spot the rule for the pattern.

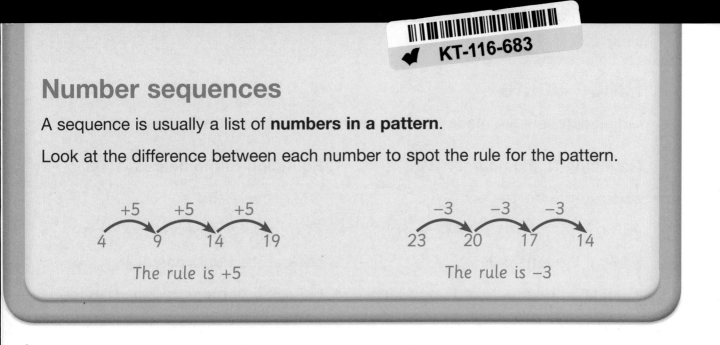

| +5 | +5 | +5 |
| 4 | 9 | 14 | 19 |

The rule is +5

| −3 | −3 | −3 |
| 23 | 20 | 17 | 14 |

The rule is −3

1 Write the missing numbers in these sequences. What is the rule for each of them?

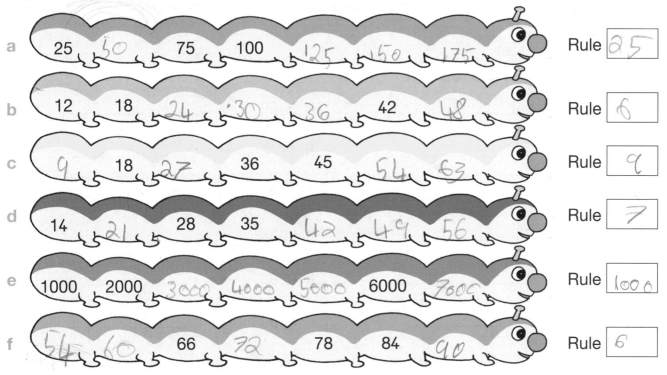

a 25, 50, 75, 100, 125, 150, 175   Rule 25

b 12, 18, 24, 30, 36, 42, 48   Rule 6

c 9, 18, 27, 36, 45, 54, 63   Rule 9

d 14, 21, 28, 35, 42, 49, 56   Rule 7

e 1000, 2000, 3000, 4000, 5000, 6000, 7000   Rule 1000

f 54, 60, 66, 72, 78, 84, 90   Rule 6

2 Negative numbers go back past zero. Write the missing numbers on these number lines.

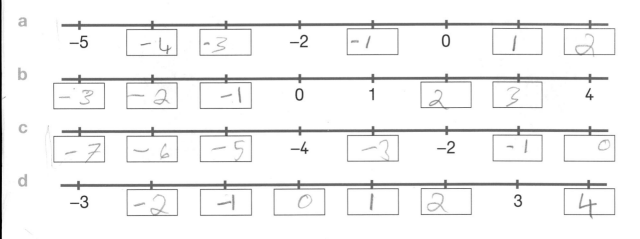

a −5, −4, −3, −2, −1, 0, 1, 2

b −3, −2, −1, 0, 1, 2, 3, 4

c −7, −6, −5, −4, −3, −2, −1, 0

d −3, −2, −1, 0, 1, 2, 3, 4

3

Place value

4-digit numbers are made from **thousands**, **hundreds**, **tens** and **ones**.

Rounding to the nearest 100

653 rounds **up** to 700

439 rounds **down** to 400

Look at the **tens** digit.

- If it is 5 or more, round up to the next hundred.

- If it is less than 5, the hundreds digit stays the same.

Rounding to the nearest 1000

4621 rounds **up** to 5000

3107 rounds **down** to 3000

Look at the **hundreds** digit.

- If it is 5 or more, round up to the next thousand.

- If it is less than 5, the thousands digit stays the same.

1 Write the value of the red digit.

a 3450 → _____5 tens_____

b 6795 → _____

c 4008 → _____

d 9217 → _____

e 3169 → _____

f 5291 → _____

g 9469 → _____

h 4778 → _____

i 7432 → _____

j 2984 → _____

k 8898 → _____

l 4793 → _____

2 Round each number to the nearest 100 or 1000.

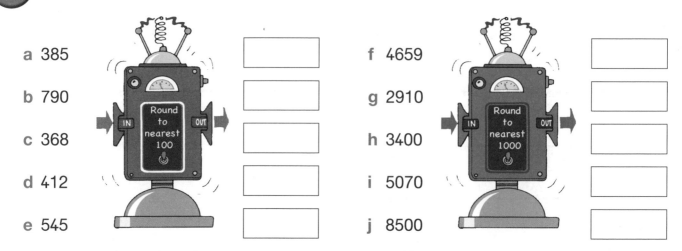

a 385

b 790

c 368

d 412

e 545

Round to nearest 100

f 4659

g 2910

h 3400

i 5070

j 8500

Round to nearest 1000

Maths

Age 8-9

Contents

Activities

Quick Tests

Paul Broadbent and Peter Patilla

Numbers to *1000*

The numbers between 100 and 999 all have **three digits**.

$$376 \rightarrow 300 + 70 + 6$$

hundreds tens ones

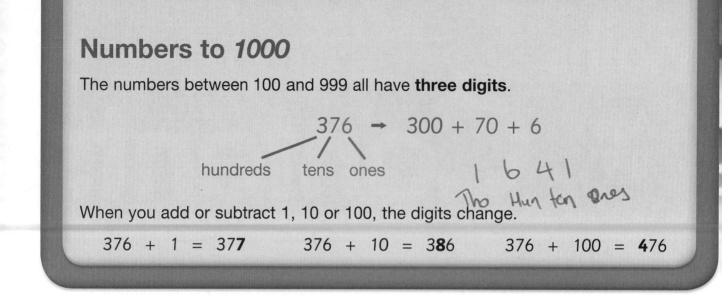

1 6 4 1
Tho Hun ten Ores

When you add or subtract 1, 10 or 100, the digits change.

| 376 + 1 = 37**7** | 376 + 10 = 3**8**6 | 376 + 100 = **4**76 |

1 Continue these number chains.

a 757 → (+ 1) → 758 → (+ 1) → 759 → (+ 1) → 760

b 628 → (− 10) → 618 → (− 10) → 608 → (− 10) → 598

c 496 → (+ 10) → 506 → (+ 10) → 516 → (+ 10) → 526

d 641 → (+ 1000) → 1641 → (+ 1000) → 2641 → (+ 1000) → 3641

e 385 → (− 100) → 285 → (− 100) → 185 → (− 100) → 85

f 9030 → (− 1000) → 8030 → (− 1000) → 7030 → (− 1000) → 608

2 Complete this number puzzle.

Across

1 Seven hundred and forty-three

5 Nine hundred and twenty

6 Eight thousand and seventy-four

Down

2 Four hundred and nine

3 Three hundred and fifty-one

4 Six hundred and eight

7 Nine thousand, six hundred and four

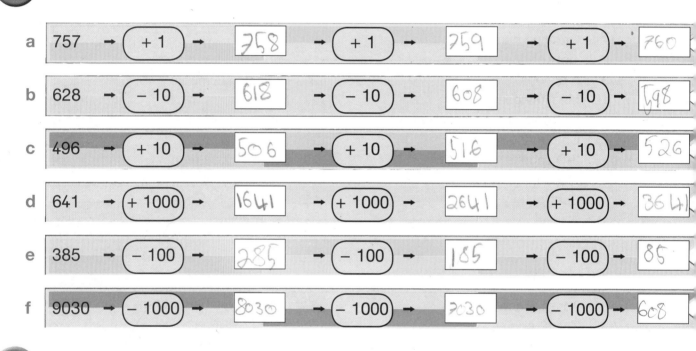

Addition

When you add numbers, decide whether to use a **mental method** or
a **written method**.

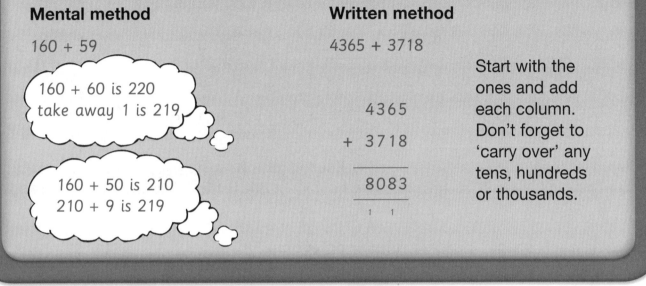

Mental method

160 + 59

160 + 60 is 220
take away 1 is 219

160 + 50 is 210
210 + 9 is 219

Written method

4365 + 3718

```
   4365
+  3718
───────
   8083
   1   1
```

Start with the
ones and add
each column.
Don't forget to
'carry over' any
tens, hundreds
or thousands.

Use the numbers from the grid to answer these.

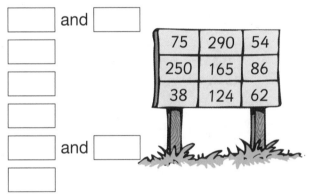

75	290	54
250	165	86
38	124	62

a Which two numbers total 140? ☐ and ☐

b What is the sum of the two largest numbers? ☐

c What is the total of the three smallest numbers? ☐

d What is the sum of the four corner numbers? ☐

e Which two numbers add up to 210? ☐ and ☐

f What is the sum of the numbers in the top row? ☐

Use a written method to answer these.

a
```
   5094
+  3168
───────
```

c
```
   4816
+  1247
───────
```

e
```
  £17.90
+ £28.54
───────
```

g
```
  £35.29
+ £13.46
───────
```

b
```
   3629
+  8294
───────
```

d
```
   1498
+  7527
───────
```

f
```
  £87.91
+ £48.14
───────
```

h
```
  £38.54
+ £27.86
───────
```

2-D shapes

A **polygon** is any 2-D shape with straight sides.

Count the number of sides to help name different polygons.

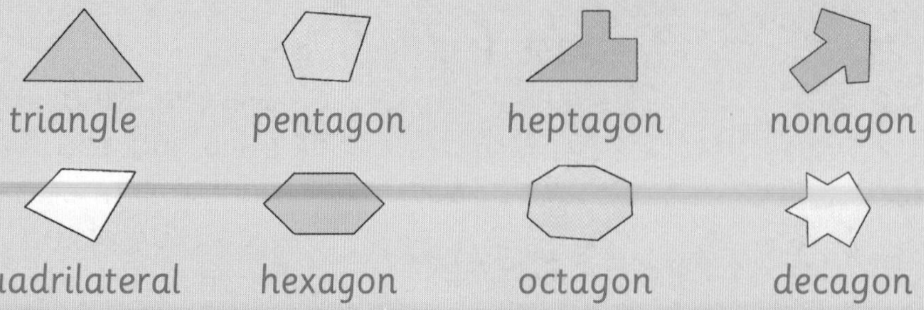

triangle   pentagon   heptagon   nonagon

quadrilateral   hexagon   octagon   decagon

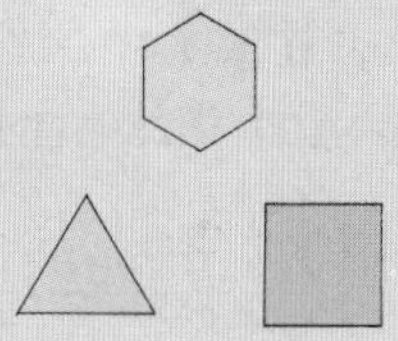

A regular polygon has equal sides and equal angles.

1 Name each shape. Tick the regular polygons.

a ☐ _____

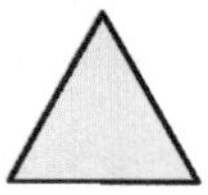

b ☐ _____

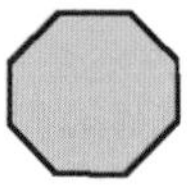

c ☐ _____

d ☐ _____

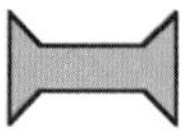

e ☐ _____

f ☐ _____

g ☐ _____

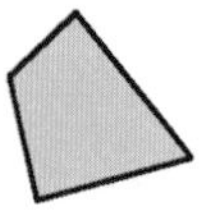

h ☐ _____

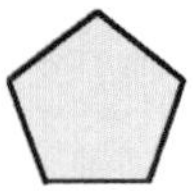

i ☐ _____

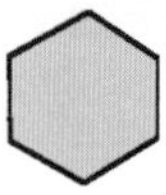

j ☐ _____

k ☐ _____

l ☐ _____

2 Use a pencil and a ruler to draw each of the named shapes accurately.
One line in each shape is already drawn.

a

rectangle

b

hexagon

c

octagon

d

right-angled
triangle

e

square

f

equilateral
triangle

g

regular pentagon

h

heptagon

Ordering numbers

To help work out the order of numbers, write them in a list. Make sure you line up the ones column.

7290   729

792   7209

Look at the numbers.
Compare the **thousands**,
then the **hundreds**, then
the **tens** and finally the
ones column.

729
792
7209
7290

1 Write these in order, starting with the smallest.

a
£1090
£1900
£958
£2850
£2589

b
3755 km
965 km
3095 km
3520 km
2830 km

c
2046 g
2460 g
2604 g
1599 g
1995 g

d
7025 ml
4599 ml
7529 ml
4600 ml
7028 ml

_____ _____ _____ _____
_____ _____ _____ _____
_____ _____ _____ _____
_____ _____ _____ _____
_____ _____ _____ _____

2 Use the digits  **2 9 3 8**

Make as many different 4-digit numbers as you can. Write them in order, starting with the smallest.

Time of day

There are 60 minutes in an hour and 24 hours in a day.

am stands for **ante meridiem** and means **before midday**.

pm stands for **post meridiem** and means **after midday**.

5.35am

35 minutes past 5
in the morning

7.15pm

15 minutes past 7
in the evening

---

1 Draw the hands on the clock or write the digital time for each start and finish time.

Start   **Finish**

a Mark goes swimming at 10.15am. He gets home 1½ hours later.

b A train leaves London at 6.20pm. It arrives at Leeds 2 hours 20 minutes later.

c Becky goes shopping at 11.10am. She finishes 3 hours 45 minutes later.

d A football match starts at 1.45pm. It finishes 90 minutes later.

---

2 This timetable shows the times of buses. If you are at a bus stop at these times, how long will you have to wait?

BUS TIMETABLE

7.40am	8.15am	9.20am	10.50am	11.40am
2.10pm	4.30pm	5.10pm	6.30pm	8.00pm

a 9.05am   = _____ minutes

b 11.15am = _____ minutes

c 5.05pm   = _____ minutes

d 10.35am = _____ minutes

e 7.40pm   = _____ minutes

f 4.45pm   = _____ minutes

Fractions

There are **two numbers** that show a fraction:

$$\frac{2}{3} \quad \begin{array}{l} \rightarrow numerator \\ \\ \rightarrow denominator \end{array}$$

The **denominator** shows the number of equal parts.

The **numerator** shows how many of the equal parts are used.

Equivalent fractions are worth the same.

$$\frac{2}{3} = \frac{4}{6} = \frac{8}{12}$$

We usually write fractions using the smallest possible denominator.

---

1 Complete the equivalent fractions. In a-d use the diagram to help you complete the first fraction.

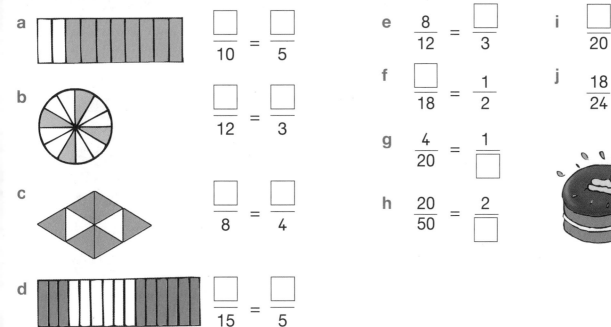

a $\frac{\square}{10} = \frac{\square}{5}$

b $\frac{\square}{12} = \frac{\square}{3}$

c $\frac{\square}{8} = \frac{\square}{4}$

d $\frac{\square}{15} = \frac{\square}{5}$

e $\frac{8}{12} = \frac{\square}{3}$

f $\frac{\square}{18} = \frac{1}{2}$

g $\frac{4}{20} = \frac{1}{\square}$

h $\frac{20}{50} = \frac{2}{\square}$

i $\frac{\square}{20} = \frac{9}{10}$

j $\frac{18}{24} = \frac{3}{\square}$

2 Write these fractions in order, starting with the smallest. Use the wall to help you.

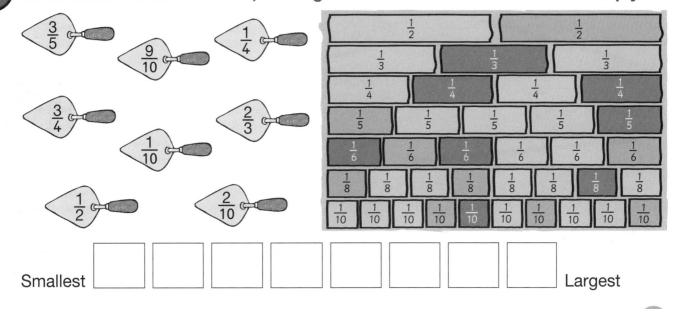

Smallest □ □ □ □ □ □ □ □ □ Largest

9

Measuring length

Look at these lengths.

10 millimetres (mm)	= 1 centimetre (cm)
100 cm	= 1 metre (m)
1000 m	= 1 kilometre (km)

Short lengths can be measured in millimetres.

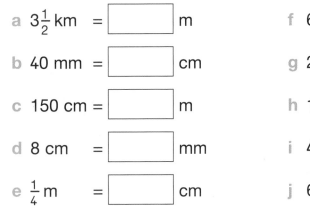

Long distances can be measured in kilometres.

1 Write these equivalent lengths.

a $3\frac{1}{2}$ km = [ ] m

b 40 mm = [ ] cm

c 150 cm = [ ] m

d 8 cm = [ ] mm

e $\frac{1}{4}$ m = [ ] cm

f 6500 m = [ ] km

g 22 cm = [ ] mm

h 18 km = [ ] m

i $4\frac{3}{4}$ m = [ ] cm

j 65 mm = [ ] cm

2 Use a ruler to measure these lines in millimetres.

a [ ] mm

b [ ] mm

c [ ] mm

d [ ] mm

e [ ] mm

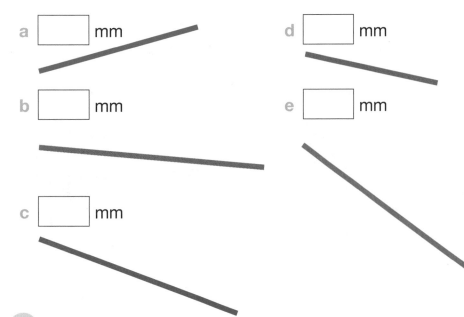

Multiplication and division

Multiplication and division are **linked**.

$6 \times 5 = 30$ If you know this, there are three other facts you also know.

$5 \times 6 = 30$
$30 \div 5 = 6$
$30 \div 6 = 5$

The three numbers 6, 5 and 30 are sometimes called a trio.

1 Write four facts for each of these trios.

a ⟨24⟩ ⟨3⟩ ⟨8⟩

☐ × ☐ = ☐

☐ × ☐ = ☐

☐ ÷ ☐ = ☐

☐ ÷ ☐ = ☐

b ⟨28⟩ ⟨7⟩ ⟨4⟩

☐ × ☐ = ☐

☐ × ☐ = ☐

☐ ÷ ☐ = ☐

☐ ÷ ☐ = ☐

Write the missing numbers.

c ☐ × 6 = 36

d ☐ ÷ 3 = 7

e 54 ÷ ☐ = 9

f 4 × ☐ = 48

g 8 × ☐ = 32

h 45 ÷ ☐ = 9

i ☐ ÷ 7 = 11

j ☐ × 6 = 48

2 If a number cannot be divided exactly, it leaves a remainder. Draw a line to join each division to its matching remainder.

60 ÷ 9

80 ÷ 3

93 ÷ 10

38 ÷ 6

37 ÷ 3

53 ÷ 6

89 ÷ 5

106 ÷ 10

48 ÷ 5

61 ÷ 2

65 ÷ 6

46 ÷ 6

11

Comparing numbers

The symbols > and < are used to compare numbers.

<

means 'is less than'

729 < 750

729 is less than 750

>

means 'is greater than'

2500 > 2100

2500 is greater than 2100

1 Write the signs > or < for each pair of numbers.

a   455 ☐ 396

b   817 ☐ 870

c   958 ☐ 936

d   1904 ☐ 2301

e   1850 ☐ 1508

f   2001 ☐ 1998

g   3750 ☐ 3079

h   6002 ☐ 6010

i   5299 ☐ 5300

j   7451 ☐ 7415

k   5306 ☐ 5311

l   9038 ☐ 9009

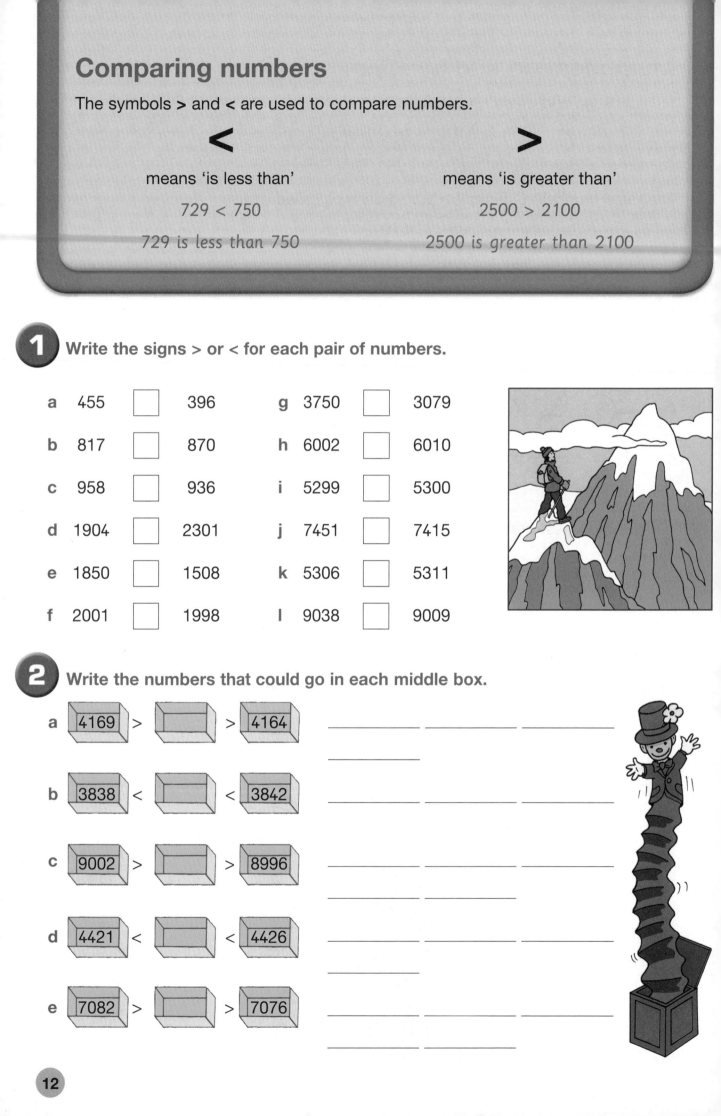

2 Write the numbers that could go in each middle box.

a   4169 > ☐ > 4164   _____ _____ _____
    _____

b   3838 < ☐ < 3842   _____ _____ _____

c   9002 > ☐ > 8996   _____ _____ _____
    _____

d   4421 < ☐ < 4426   _____ _____ _____
    _____

e   7082 > ☐ > 7076   _____ _____ _____
    _____

3-D shapes

A **polyhedron** is a 3-D shape with flat faces.

A cube is a polyhedron. It has:

- 8 vertices (corners)
- 12 edges
- 6 faces.

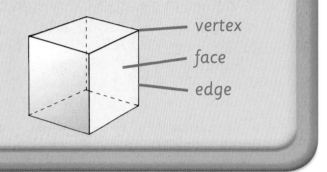

vertex

face

edge

1 Name each shape. Choose the correct word from the box.

cylinder
cone
cube
pyramid
sphere
cuboid

a _____

b _____

c _____

d _____

e _____

f _____

2 Write how many faces, edges and vertices each shape has.

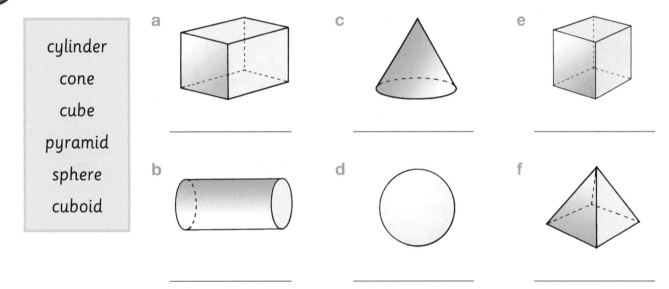

	faces	edges	vertices
a	_____	_____	_____
b	_____	_____	_____
c	_____	_____	_____
d	_____	_____	_____

13

Measuring mass

Kilograms (kg) and **grams** (g) are some of the units we use to measure the weight or mass of an object.

1000 g = 1 kg   250 g = $\frac{1}{4}$ kg

500 g = $\frac{1}{2}$ kg   750 g = $\frac{3}{4}$ kg

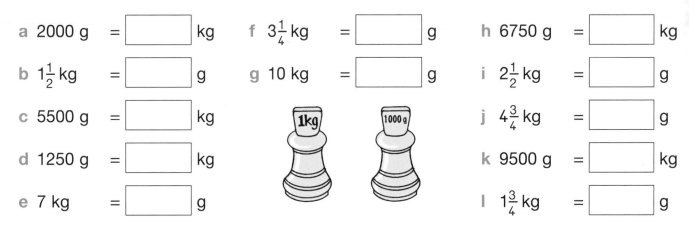

1 Write these equivalent units.

a 2000 g = ☐ kg   f $3\frac{1}{4}$ kg = ☐ g   h 6750 g = ☐ kg

b $1\frac{1}{2}$ kg = ☐ g   g 10 kg = ☐ g   i $2\frac{1}{2}$ kg = ☐ g

c 5500 g = ☐ kg   j $4\frac{3}{4}$ kg = ☐ g

d 1250 g = ☐ kg   k 9500 g = ☐ kg

e 7 kg = ☐ g   l $1\frac{3}{4}$ kg = ☐ g

2 Look at these scales. Write the mass shown in kilograms.

a

_____

b

_____

c

_____

Write the mass shown in grams.

d

_____

e

_____

f

_____

14

Subtraction

If you cannot **subtract** numbers mentally, use a written method. Look at these two methods for 734 − 278.

Number line method

2 + 20 + 434 = 456

278 onto 280 is 2. 280 onto 300 is 20. 300 onto 734 is 434.

Column method

$$\begin{array}{r} {}^{6}\cancel{7}{}^{12}\cancel{3}{}^{1}4 \\ -\ 2\ 7\ 8 \\ \hline 4\ 5\ 6 \end{array}$$

- Start with the ones column, taking away the bottom number from the top.
- If the top number is smaller than the bottom, exchange a ten or a hundred.

Choose a method to answer these.

a Find the difference between 184 and 367.

b What is 253 subtract 176?

c What is 852 take away 483?

d Decrease 813 by 125.

e Subtract 218 from 1186.

f What is the difference between 2084 and 2257?

g What is 1437 minus 1185?

h What number is 2425 less than 3812?

Write the digits 2 to 9 on small squares of paper. Arrange them on these squares as subtractions so you can answer these.

☐☐☐☐ − ☐☐☐☐

2 3 4
5   6
7 8 9

a What is the biggest answer you can make?   =

b What is the smallest answer you can make?   =

c Give an answer as near as possible to 2000.

☐☐☐☐ − ☐☐☐☐ = ☐☐☐☐

Area

The area of a shape can be found by **counting squares on a grid**.

Count half squares for shapes with straight diagonal sides.

For irregular shapes, count the squares that are covered more than half.

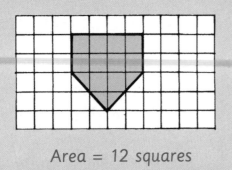

Area = 12 squares

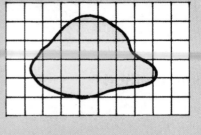

Area = approximately 19 squares

1 Work out the area of each shape.

a Area = [ ] squares

b Area = [ ] squares

c Area = [ ] squares

2 Draw two different rectangles with an area of 8 squares.

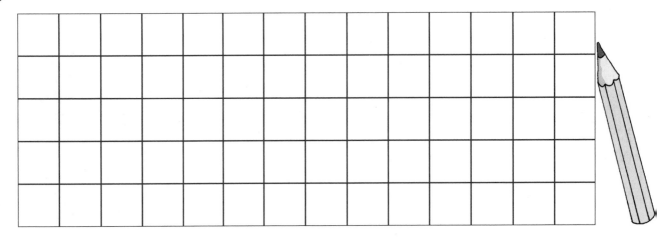

Written multiplication and division

Here are two methods of **multiplication**.

Here is a method of **division**.

Grid method

47×6

	6
40	240
7	42

282

Column method

47×6

```
    4 7
  ×   6
  -----
  2 8 2
  -----
    4
```

$197 \div 6$

```
        32 remainder 5
    6 | 1 9 7
      - 1 8 0
      -------
          1 7
        -  1 2
        -------
            5
```

Use one of the methods above to answer these multiplication sums.

Working out

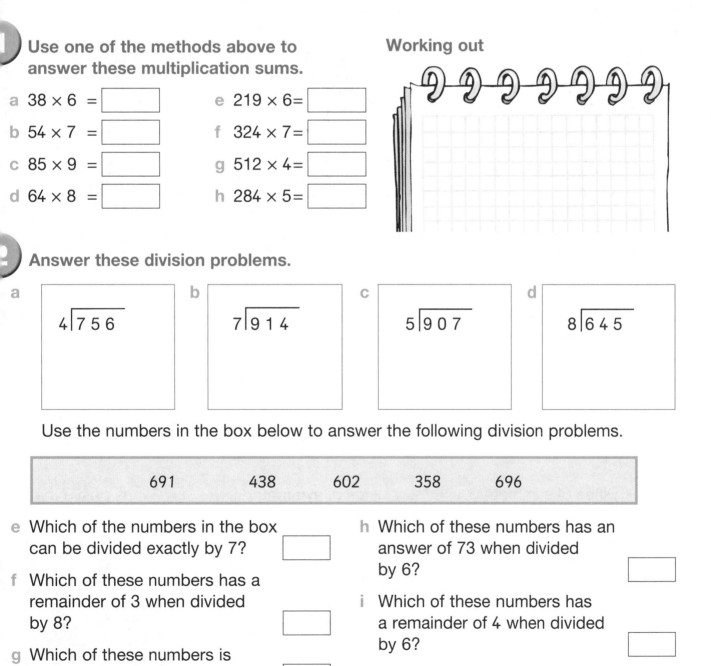

a $38 \times 6 = \boxed{}$

b $54 \times 7 = \boxed{}$

c $85 \times 9 = \boxed{}$

d $64 \times 8 = \boxed{}$

e $219 \times 6 = \boxed{}$

f $324 \times 7 = \boxed{}$

g $512 \times 4 = \boxed{}$

h $284 \times 5 = \boxed{}$

Answer these division problems.

a $4 | 7\,5\,6$

b $7 | 9\,1\,4$

c $5 | 9\,0\,7$

d $8 | 6\,4\,5$

Use the numbers in the box below to answer the following division problems.

| 691 | 438 | 602 | 358 | 696 |

e Which of the numbers in the box can be divided exactly by 7? $\boxed{}$

f Which of these numbers has a remainder of 3 when divided by 8? $\boxed{}$

g Which of these numbers is exactly divisible by 4? $\boxed{}$

h Which of these numbers has an answer of 73 when divided by 6? $\boxed{}$

i Which of these numbers has a remainder of 4 when divided by 6? $\boxed{}$

Symmetry

A shape is symmetrical if both sides are exactly the same either side of a **mirror line**, like a reflection.

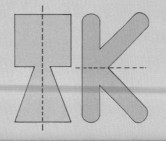

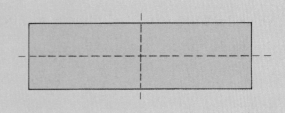

This rectangle has two lines of symmetry.

1 Draw the reflection of each of these.

a

c

e

b

d

f

2 Draw lines of symmetry on these shapes. Write the number of lines of symmetry for each shape.

a

[ ] lines of symmetry

c

[ ] lines of symmetry

e

[ ] lines of symmetry

b

[ ] lines of symmetry

d

[ ] lines of symmetry

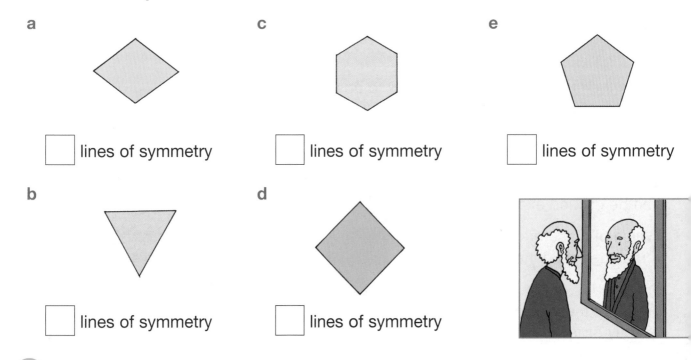

Measuring capacity

Litres (l) and **millilitres** (ml) are some of the units we use to measure the capacity of liquids in containers.

$$1000 \text{ ml} = 1 \text{ l} \qquad 750 \text{ ml} = \tfrac{3}{4} \text{ l}$$
$$250 \text{ ml} = \tfrac{1}{4} \text{ l} \qquad 500 \text{ ml} = \tfrac{1}{2} \text{ l}$$

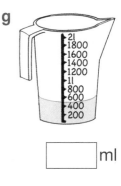

1 Write the equivalent units.

a 3000 ml = [   ] l

b $1\tfrac{1}{2}$ l = [   ] ml

c 6 l = [   ] ml

d 2250 ml = [   ] l

e 1750 ml = [   ] l

f 10 l = [   ] ml

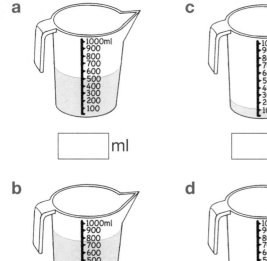

g $3\tfrac{1}{2}$ l = [   ] ml

h 2000 ml = [   ] l

i 4500 ml = [   ] l

j $8\tfrac{3}{4}$ l = [   ] ml

k 5750 ml = [   ] l

l $6\tfrac{3}{4}$ l = [   ] ml

2 Write the capacity each jug shows in millilitres.

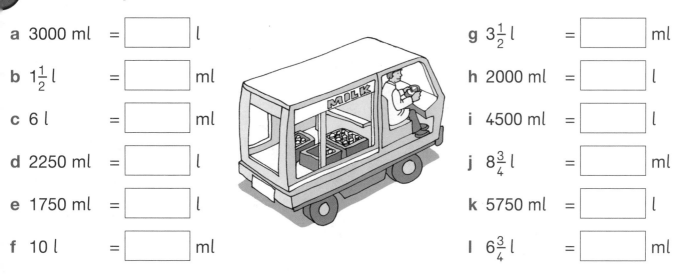

a [   ] ml

b [   ] ml

c [   ] ml

d [   ] ml

e [   ] ml

f [   ] ml

g [   ] ml

h [   ] ml

Decimals

A **decimal point** is used to separate whole numbers from fractions.

$$0.1 = \frac{1}{10}$$

$$0.5 = \frac{5}{10} = \frac{1}{2}$$

$$1.03 = 1\frac{3}{100}$$

$$4.76 = 4\frac{76}{100}$$

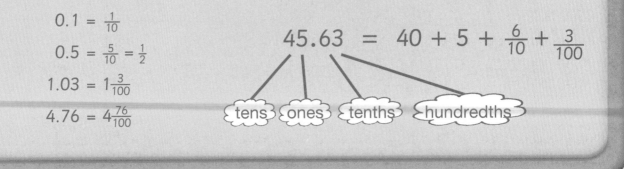

$$45.63 = 40 + 5 + \frac{6}{10} + \frac{3}{100}$$

tens   ones   tenths   hundredths

1 Change these fractions to decimals.

a $\frac{3}{10}$ =

b $\frac{5}{10}$ =

c $\frac{2}{10}$ =

d $\frac{3}{4}$ =

e $\frac{17}{100}$ =

f $\frac{4}{10}$ =

g $\frac{41}{100}$ =

h $\frac{9}{10}$ =

i $\frac{65}{100}$ =

j $\frac{1}{2}$ =

k $\frac{59}{100}$ =

l $\frac{1}{4}$ =

2 Write the decimals on these number lines.

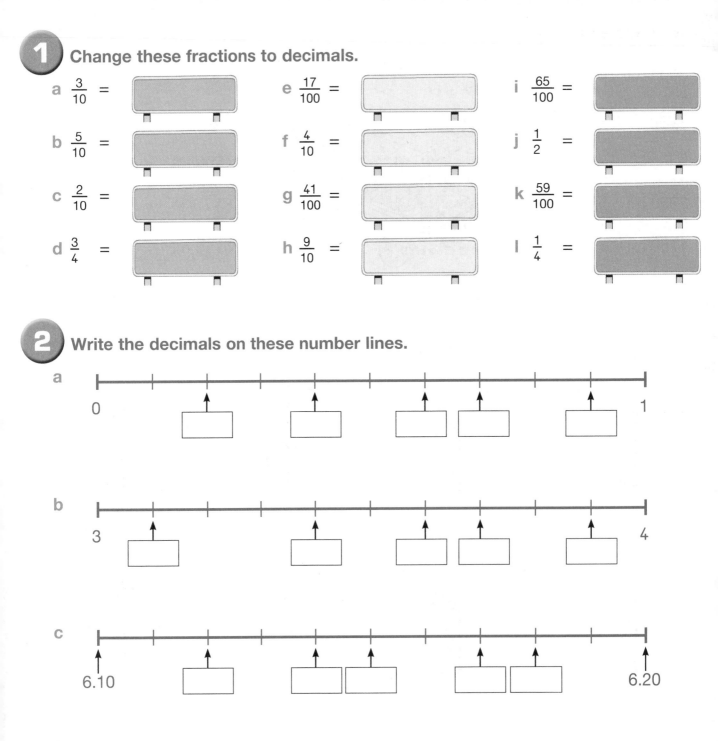

a   0   1

b   3   4

c   6.10   6.20

Reading bar charts

A **bar chart** shows information as a graph.

Read the scale and labels on the axes carefully.

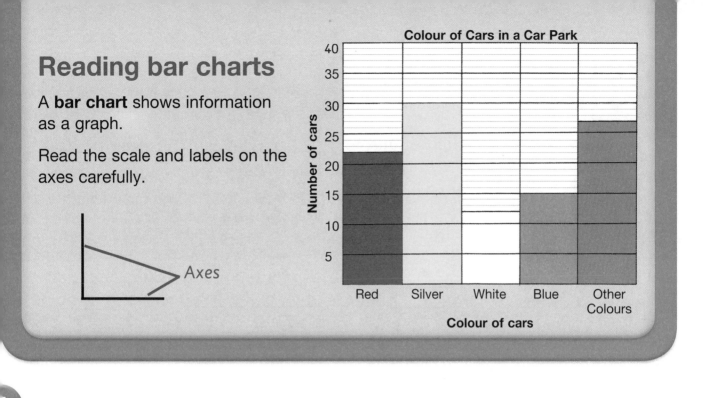

Axes

Colour of Cars in a Car Park

1 Look at the graph above and answer these.

a Which colour was the most common car colour in the car park? _____

b How many cars were white? _____

c How many more cars were red than white? _____

d Which colour had half the number of silver cars? _____

e Black was the most common 'Other colour', with $\frac{1}{3}$ of these cars black. How many cars in total were black? _____

f How many cars in total were in the car park? _____

2 This graph shows the number of cars visiting a car wash over five days.

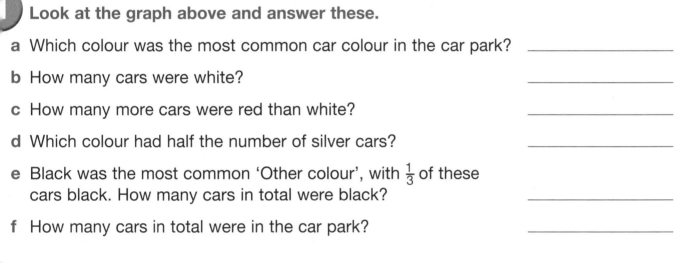

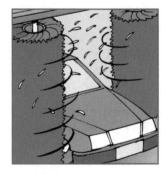

a How many cars visited the car wash on Tuesday? _____

b On which day did 38 cars visit the car wash? _____

c How many more cars visited on Friday than Monday? _____

d On which day did 15 fewer cars visit the car wash than on Tuesday? _____

Triangles

Learn the names of different types of triangle.

Equilateral triangle	Right-angled triangle	Isosceles triangle	Scalene triangle
3 equal sides and 3 equal angles	1 right angle	2 equal sides 2 equal angles	No sides the same length

1 Colour each triangle to match the key. Use a ruler to help you decide.

Key:

equilateral

isosceles

scalene

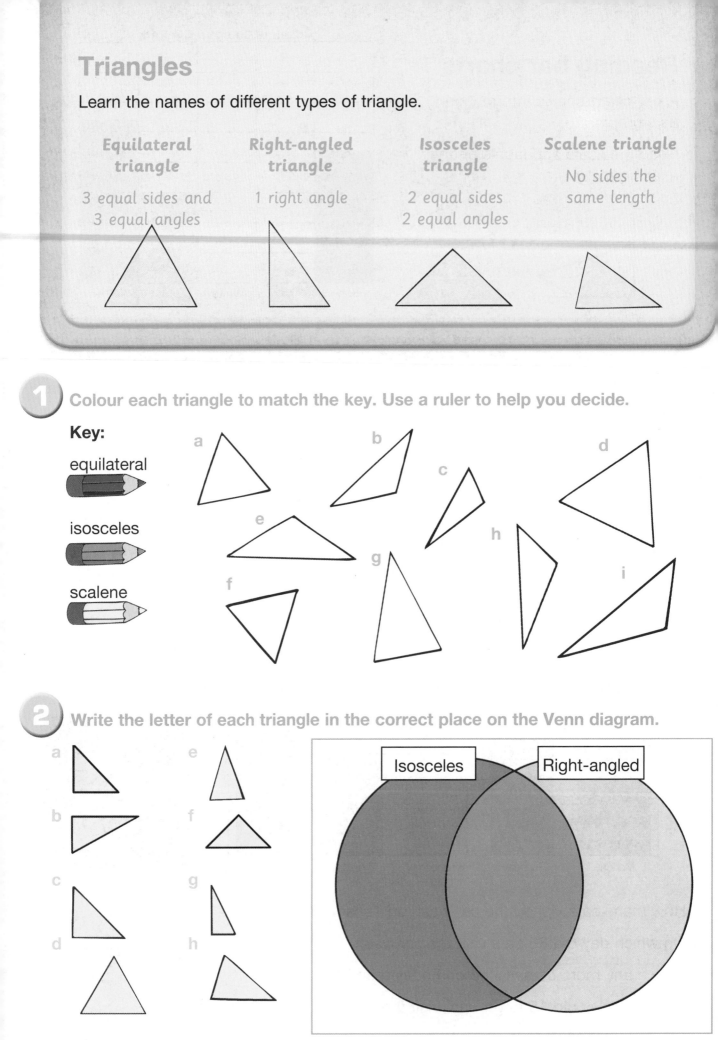

2 Write the letter of each triangle in the correct place on the Venn diagram.

Isosceles   Right-angled

Equivalent fractions

Fractions that have the **same value** are called equivalent fractions.

$\frac{5}{10}$ is the same as $\frac{1}{2}$

$\frac{1}{3}$ is the same as $\frac{2}{6}$

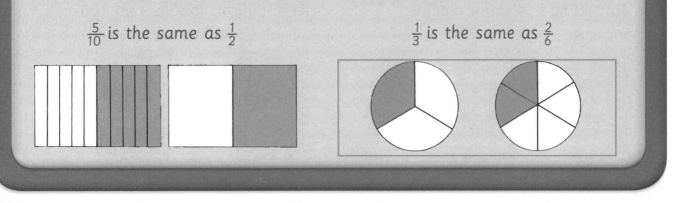

1 Complete the equivalent fractions. In a–d use the diagrams to help you complete the first fraction.

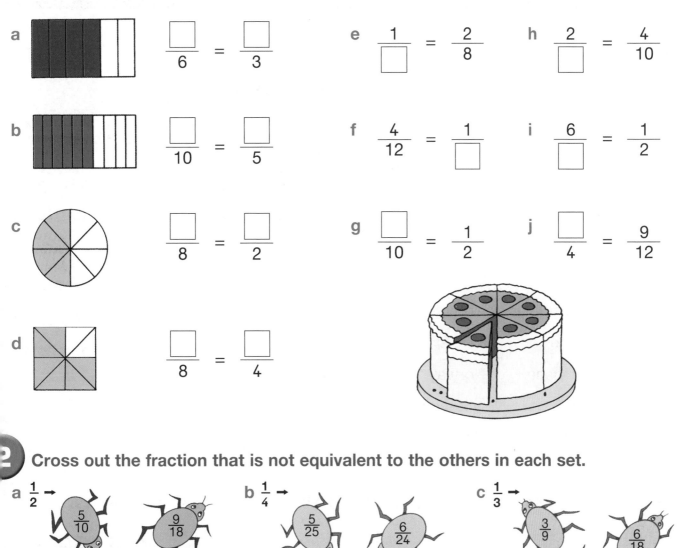

a $\dfrac{\square}{6} = \dfrac{\square}{3}$

b $\dfrac{\square}{10} = \dfrac{\square}{5}$

c $\dfrac{\square}{8} = \dfrac{\square}{2}$

d $\dfrac{\square}{8} = \dfrac{\square}{4}$

e $\dfrac{1}{\square} = \dfrac{2}{8}$

f $\dfrac{4}{12} = \dfrac{1}{\square}$

g $\dfrac{\square}{10} = \dfrac{1}{2}$

h $\dfrac{2}{\square} = \dfrac{4}{10}$

i $\dfrac{6}{\square} = \dfrac{1}{2}$

j $\dfrac{\square}{4} = \dfrac{9}{12}$

2 Cross out the fraction that is not equivalent to the others in each set.

a $\frac{1}{2}$ →

$\frac{5}{10}$ $\frac{9}{18}$ $\frac{6}{12}$ $\frac{10}{20}$ $\frac{7}{15}$

b $\frac{1}{4}$ →

$\frac{5}{25}$ $\frac{6}{24}$ $\frac{10}{40}$ $\frac{4}{16}$ $\frac{3}{12}$

c $\frac{1}{3}$ →

$\frac{3}{9}$ $\frac{6}{18}$ $\frac{4}{12}$ $\frac{8}{27}$ $\frac{10}{30}$

23

Rounding numbers

1 This chart shows a list of some of the highest waterfalls in the world. Round each height to the nearest 10 m and 100 m.

Waterfall	Country	Total drop (m)	Rounded to the: Nearest 10 m	Nearest 100 m
Angel	Venezuela	979	_____	_____
Tugela	South Africa	947	_____	_____
Mongefossen	Norway	774	_____	_____
Yosemite	USA	739	_____	_____
Tyssestrengane	Norway	646	_____	_____
Sutherland	New Zealand	581	_____	_____
Kjellfossen	Norway	561	_____	_____

2 Round these to the nearest 10 or 100 to work out approximate answers.

a 73 + 89 → ☐

b 17 × 9 → ☐

c 346 − 152 → ☐

d 509 + 296 → ☐

e 256 + 799 → ☐

f 509 − 296 → ☐

Multiples

Multiples are the numbers in the **times tables**.

Multiples of 2 are 2, 4, 6, 8, 10, 12 and so on.

Multiples of 5 are 5, 10, 15, 20, 25 and so on.

Multiples of a number do not come to an end at ×12, they go on and on.
For example 52, 98, 114, 230 are all multiples of 2.

1 Write these numbers in the correct boxes. Some of them will belong in more than one box.

48   56   100   39   86   52   82   42   63   85   70   115   60   65

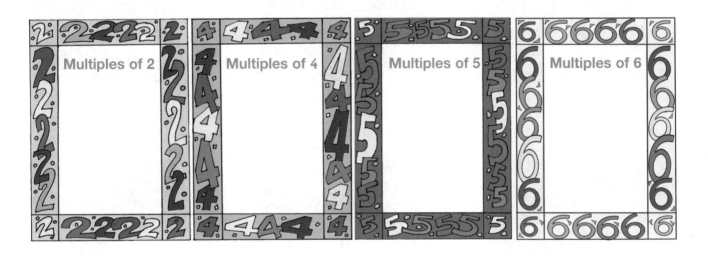

Multiples of 2 | Multiples of 4 | Multiples of 5 | Multiples of 6

2 Colour all the multiples of 3 red.
Colour all the multiples of 5 blue.
What patterns do you see on the grid?

1	2	3	4	5	6	7	8	9	10
11	12	13	14	15	16	17	18	19	20
21	22	23	24	25	26	27	28	29	30
31	32	33	34	35	36	37	38	39	40
41	42	43	44	45	46	47	48	49	50
51	52	53	54	55	56	57	58	59	60
61	62	63	64	65	66	67	68	69	70
71	72	73	74	75	76	77	78	79	80
81	82	83	84	85	86	87	88	89	90
91	92	93	94	95	96	97	98	99	100

Money problems

If you need to find the **difference** between two amounts, count on from the lower amount.

+30p   +£1   +60p

£1.70   £2.00   £3.00   £3.60

The difference between £1.70 and £3.60 is £1.90 (30p + £1 + 60p)

You can work out an amount of change in this way as well.

1 Work out these price differences.

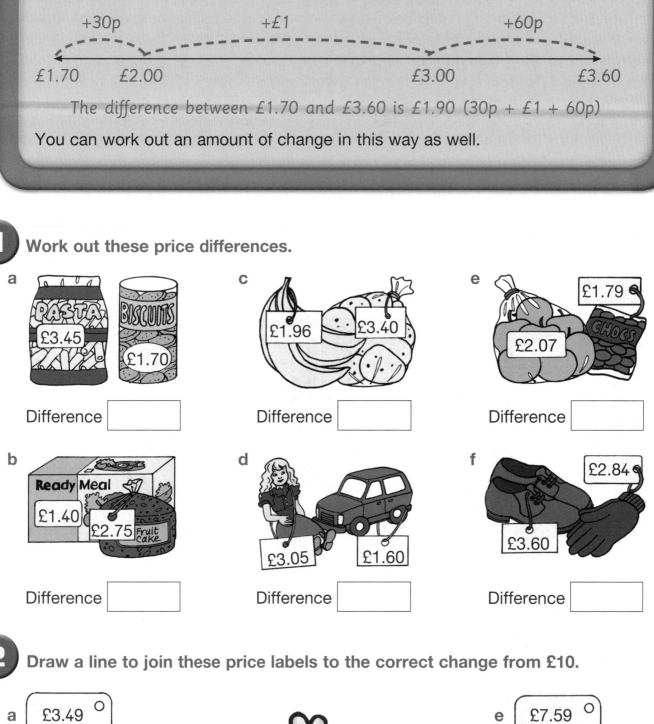

a

£3.45   £1.70

Difference [ ]

b

Ready Meal

£1.40   £2.75 Fruit Cake

Difference [ ]

c

£1.96   £3.40

Difference [ ]

d

£3.05   £1.60

Difference [ ]

e

£1.79   £2.07

Difference [ ]

f

£2.84   £3.60

Difference [ ]

2 Draw a line to join these price labels to the correct change from £10.

a £3.49

b £8.99

c £7.89

d £3.69

£1.01   £3.41

£2.11   £6.51   £1.11

£6.31   £2.41   £2.61

e £7.59

f £8.89

g £7.39

h £6.59

Angles

90° is a quarter turn, or a **right angle**.

An **acute angle** is less than 90°.

A **straight line** is 180°.

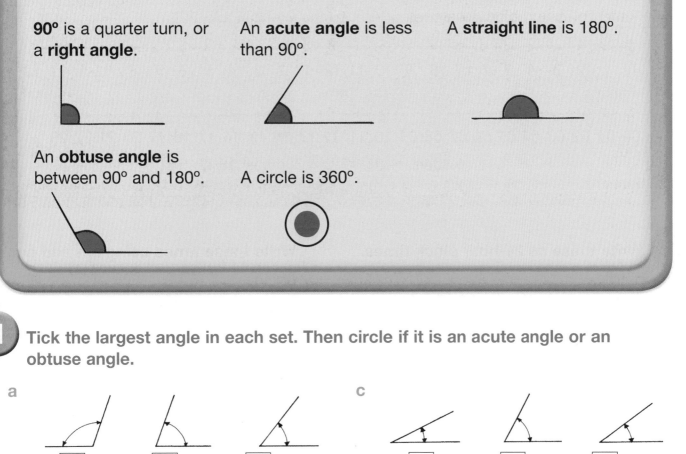

An **obtuse angle** is between 90° and 180°.

A circle is 360°.

---

1 Tick the largest angle in each set. Then circle if it is an acute angle or an obtuse angle.

a

☐ ☐ ☐

acute angle   obtuse angle

c

☐ ☐ ☐

acute angle   obtuse angle

b

☐ ☐ ☐

acute angle   obtuse angle

d

☐ ☐ ☐

acute angle   obtuse angle

---

2 These are the eight compass directions. Write the direction you will face after turning.

a Start facing north. Turn 90° clockwise. _____

b Start facing west. Turn 180° anticlockwise. _____

c Start facing south. Turn 45° clockwise. _____

d Start facing east. Turn 360° anticlockwise. _____

e Start facing north-east. Turn 90° clockwise. _____

f Start facing north-west. Turn 45° anticlockwise. _____

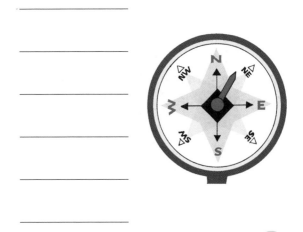

24-hour clock time

Timetables and digital watches often use the **24-hour clock** time.

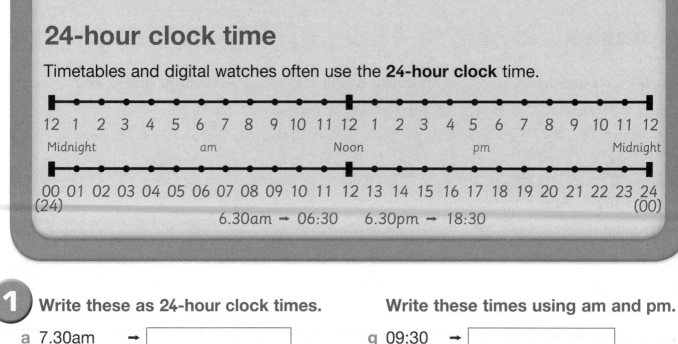

6.30am → 06:30   6.30pm → 18:30

1 **Write these as 24-hour clock times.**

a 7.30am → ☐

b 9.00pm → ☐

c 10.15am → ☐

d 4.45pm → ☐

e 2.10am → ☐

f 11.50pm → ☐

Write these times using am and pm.

g 09:30 → ☐

h 15:00 → ☐

i 20:15 → ☐

j 13:40 → ☐

k 10:55 → ☐

l 22:20 → ☐

2 **Answer these questions about the marathon race.**

a How long did it take Tom to run the race?

_____

b How long did it take Jill to run the race

_____

c How long did it take Jack to run the race?

_____

d How much longer did Jill take than Jack to finish the race?

_____

RESULTS		
Name	Start Time	Finish Time
Tom	10:20	14:35
Jill	10:25	14:05
Jack	10:30	13:20

Handling data

Data can be shown on graphs.
Graphs have **axes** and a **scale**.

Read the scale and labels on the axes carefully.

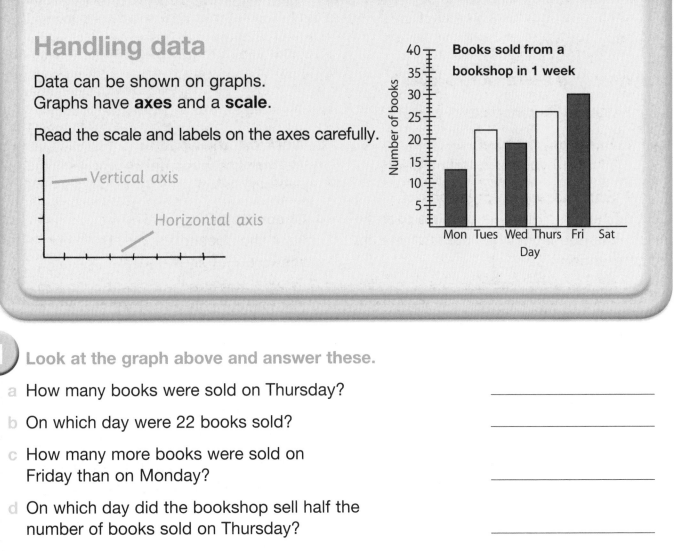

Vertical axis

Horizontal axis

Look at the graph above and answer these.

a How many books were sold on Thursday? _____

b On which day were 22 books sold? _____

c How many more books were sold on
Friday than on Monday? _____

d On which day did the bookshop sell half the
number of books sold on Thursday? _____

e On Saturday, the bookshop sold as many books
as the total number of books sold on Monday and
Tuesday. Show this on the graph. _____

f How many books were sold in total in the week,
including Saturday? _____

Carry out a word survey. Choose a page from one of your books. Count the
number of letters for each word and record it on this tally chart. Show your
results on a bar chart.

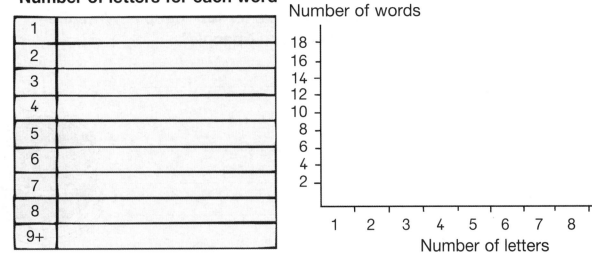

Number of letters for each word

1	
2	
3	
4	
5	
6	
7	
8	
9+	

Number of words

18
16
14
12
10
8
6
4
2

1   2   3   4   5   6   7   8   9+
Number of letters

Problems

When you read a **word problem**, try to 'picture' the problem.

Try these four steps.

1 Read the problem
What do you need to find out?

2 Sort out the calculation
There may be one or more parts to the question. What calculations are needed?

3 Work out the answer
Will you use a mental or written method?

4 Check back
Read the question again. Have you answered it fully?

1 Read these word problems and answer them.

a A bar of chocolate costs 45p. What do 4 bars cost? _____

b Sophie has 90 g of butter. She uses 35 g to make a loaf of bread. How much butter is left? _____

c A board game costs £8.40. It is reduced by £2.50 in a sale. What is the new price of the game? _____

d 68 people are going on a trip. Minibuses can take 10 people. How many minibuses will be needed? _____

e A pencil costs 19p. How many can be bought for £2? _____

f Daniel is saving up to buy a game for £42. He has £10.50 and his uncle gives him £15. How much more does he need to save? _____

g Mrs Benson travels 48 km each day to get to work and back. How far will she travel in 5 days? _____

h Jack had 18 stickers. He bought 16 more, then he gave half of his stickers to his brother. How many did he give to his brother? _____

2 These are the ingredients of a chocolate cake for four people. Write the ingredients needed for a chocolate cake for 12 people.

50 g margarine
40 g sugar
60 g flour
1 egg
15 g cocoa powder
20 ml milk

_____
_____
_____
_____
_____

Coordinates

Coordinates help to find a position on a grid.

Look at the coordinates of A and B.

Read the numbers across **horizontally** and then up **vertically** for the pair of coordinates. (2,6) and (7,3)

Look at the grid below and answer the questions.

a What letter is at position:

(2,3) ____   (8,2) ____   (10,9) ____

b What are the coordinates for

D (___,___)   A (___,___)   S (___,___)

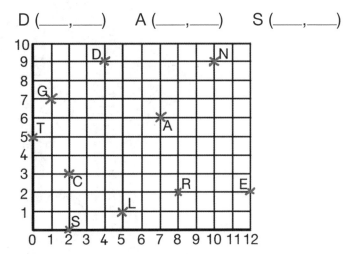

c Use the coordinates to spell out a shape and draw it in the box below.

(8,2) (12,2) (2,3) (0,5) (7,6)
(10,9) (1,7) (5,1) (12,2)

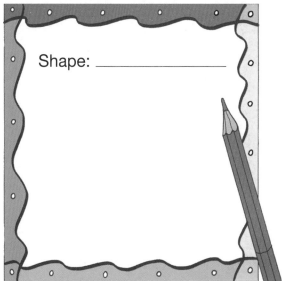

Shape: _____

Draw a quadrilateral on this grid.

The coordinates are:

(4,2) (6,5) (3,7) (1,4)

The shape is a _____.

Move two of the coordinates to make the shape into a rectangle.

Write the coordinates of your rectangle.

_____ _____

_____ _____

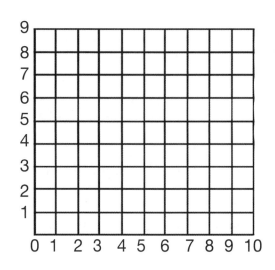

Test 1 Place value (1)

Thousands	Hundreds	Tens	Units	
4	9	5	7	= 4000 + 900 + 50 + 7

Write the missing numbers.

1. 4173 = 4000 + 100 + ☐ + 3

2. 8465 = ☐ + 400 + 60 + 5

3. 3657 = 3000 + ☐ + 50 + 7

4. 7895 = 7000 + 800 + ☐ + 5

5. 6218 = ☐ + 200 + 10 + 8

Write these as numbers.

6. two thousand one hundred and eight ☐

7. four thousand and ninety ☐

8. seven thousand two hundred and thirty-five ☐

9. three thousand eight hundred and sixteen ☐

10. nine thousand seven hundred ☐

Colour in your score

32

Test 2 Addition and subtraction (1)

Adding words

altogether   TOTAL   **sum**

add

increase   more than   **plus**

Subtracting words

less than   take away

minus   subtract   FEWER

decrease   difference

Work out the answers.

1. Add 353 to 34.

2. Total 35, 62 and 101.

3. What is the difference between 476 and 500?

4. Decrease 382 by 182.

5. What is 604 take away 418?

6. What change would you get from £5 after spending £3.44?

7. Total 1·6 m, 2·5 m and 4·1 m.

8. There were 225 ml of liquid in a jug and 60 ml was poured out. How much liquid was left?

9. Add £1.23, £2.75 and £1.35.

10. You have a 5·2 m strip of ribbon. You need 1·75 m to wrap your parcel. How much ribbon would be left?

10 9 8 7 6 5 4 3 2 1

Colour in your score

Test 3 **Measures**

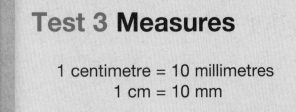

1 centimetre = 10 millimetres	1 litre = 1000 millilitres
1 cm = 10 mm	1 l = 1000 ml

1 metre = 100 centimetres	1 kilogram = 1000 grams
1 m = 100 cm	1 kg = 1000 g

1 kilometre = 1000 metres
1 km = 1000 m

Answer these questions.

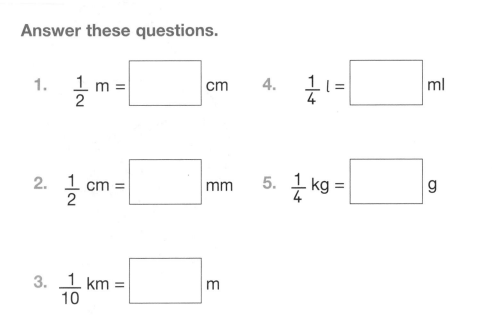

1. $\frac{1}{2}$ m = ☐ cm

4. $\frac{1}{4}$ l = ☐ ml

2. $\frac{1}{2}$ cm = ☐ mm

5. $\frac{1}{4}$ kg = ☐ g

3. $\frac{1}{10}$ km = ☐ m

Measure these lines with a ruler.

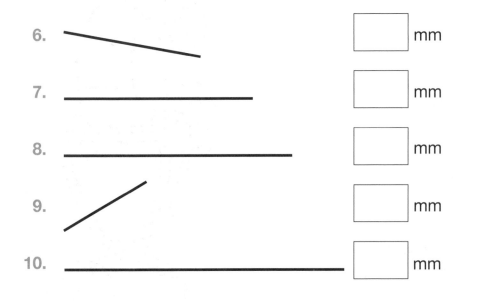

6. ☐ mm

7. ☐ mm

8. ☐ mm

9. ☐ mm

10. ☐ mm

Colour in your score

34

Test 4 2-D shapes

A **polygon** is any 2-D shape with straight sides.

A **regular polygon's** sides and angles are all equal.

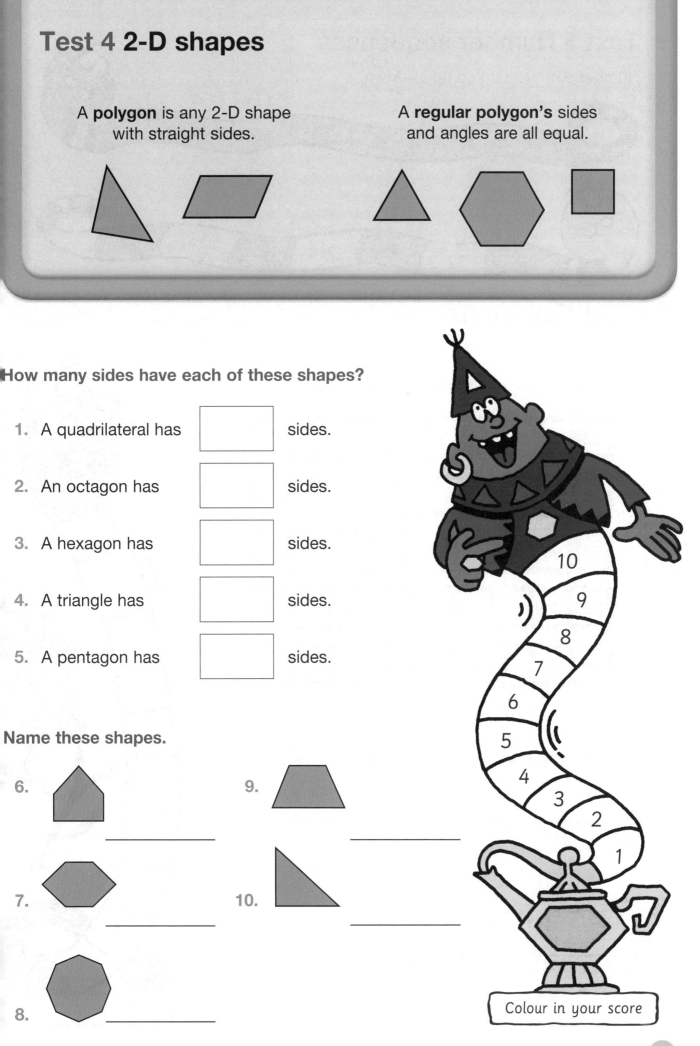

How many sides have each of these shapes?

1. A quadrilateral has [ ] sides.

2. An octagon has [ ] sides.

3. A hexagon has [ ] sides.

4. A triangle has [ ] sides.

5. A pentagon has [ ] sides.

Name these shapes.

6. _____

9. _____

7. _____

10. _____

8. _____

Colour in your score

Test 5 Number sequences

Number patterns can go up or down.

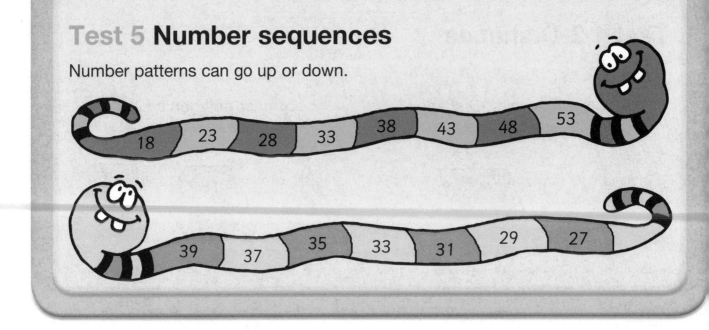

Write the missing numbers in these sequences.

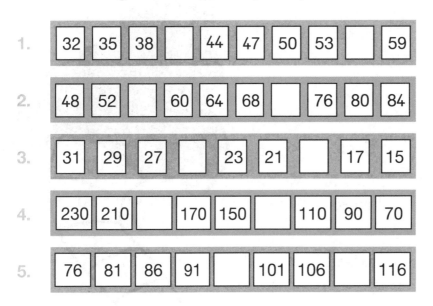

1. | 32 | 35 | 38 | | 44 | 47 | 50 | 53 | | 59 |

2. | 48 | 52 | | 60 | 64 | 68 | | 76 | 80 | 84 |

3. | 31 | 29 | 27 | | 23 | 21 | | 17 | 15 |

4. | 230 | 210 | | 170 | 150 | | 110 | 90 | 70 |

5. | 76 | 81 | 86 | 91 | | 101 | 106 | | 116 |

Write the missing numbers on these number lines.

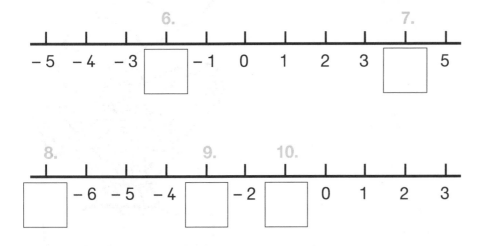

6.   7.

– 5   – 4   – 3   ☐   – 1   0   1   2   3   ☐   5

8.   9.   10.

☐   – 6   – 5   – 4   ☐   – 2   ☐   0   1   2   3

10
9
8
7
6
5
4
3
2
1

Colour in your score

36

Test 6 Multiplication tables

You need to know your **tables**.

Remember, **4 × 6** is the same as **6 × 4**.

It doesn't matter which way round you multiply.

Write the missing numbers.

1. 7 × ☐ = 35

2. ☐ × 4 = 44

3. 8 × 3 = ☐

4. ☐ × 7 = 28

5. 12 × ☐ = 60

6. 8 × ☐ = 40

7. 11 × 6 = ☐

8. ☐ × 3 = 27

9. ☐ × 6 = 72

10. 4 × ☐ = 36

Colour in your score

Test 7 Money

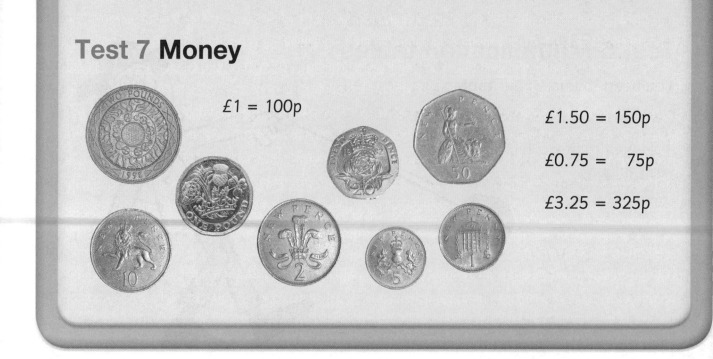

£1 = 100p

£1.50 = 150p

£0.75 = 75p

£3.25 = 325p

Convert these amounts into pounds or pence.

1. £2.35 = ☐ p   4. £1.09 = ☐ p

2. £6.45 = ☐ p   5. £ ☐ = 214p

3. £ ☐ = 370p   6. £2.75 = ☐ p

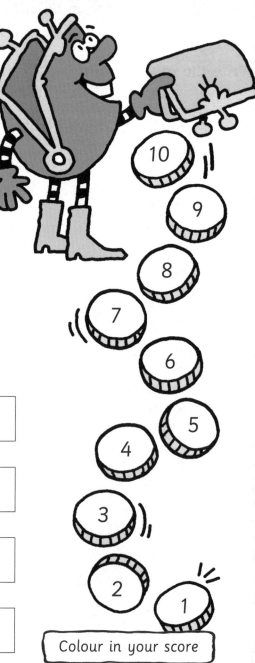

Write the totals.

7. £1.85 + 70p = £ ☐

8. 65p + £2.50 = £ ☐

9. 90p + £3.15 = £ ☐

10. £1.90 + £2.20 = £ ☐

Colour in your score

Test 8 Fractions

Fractions which are the same value are called **equivalent fractions**.

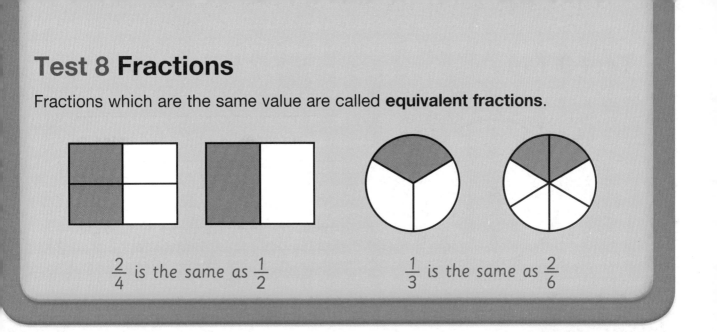

$\frac{2}{4}$ is the same as $\frac{1}{2}$

$\frac{1}{3}$ is the same as $\frac{2}{6}$

Write the fractions which are shaded.

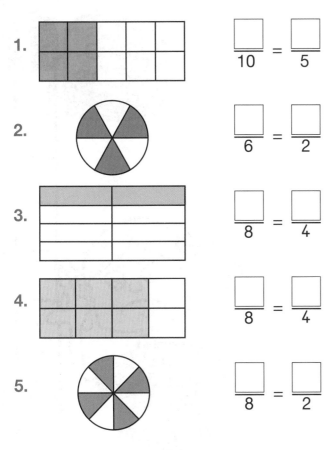

1. $\frac{\boxed{}}{10} = \frac{\boxed{}}{5}$

2. $\frac{\boxed{}}{6} = \frac{\boxed{}}{2}$

3. $\frac{\boxed{}}{8} = \frac{\boxed{}}{4}$

4. $\frac{\boxed{}}{8} = \frac{\boxed{}}{4}$

5. $\frac{\boxed{}}{8} = \frac{\boxed{}}{2}$

Complete these fractions.

6. $\frac{4}{5} = \frac{8}{\boxed{}}$

7. $\frac{2}{3} = \frac{\boxed{}}{9}$

8. $\frac{1}{\boxed{}} = \frac{3}{12}$

9. $\frac{3}{4} = \frac{\boxed{}}{12}$

10. $\frac{3}{10} = \frac{6}{\boxed{}}$

10
9
8
7
6
5
4
3
2
1

Colour in your score

39

Test 9 Time

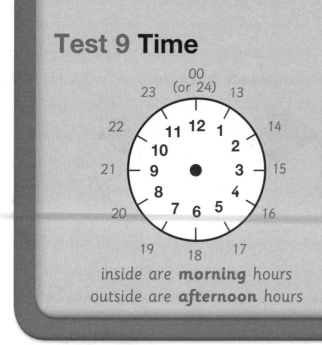

am times	pm times
morning hours	afternoon hours
midnight ⟶ noon ⟶ midnight	

inside are **morning** hours
outside are **afternoon** hours

Join the matching times.

1. 10:25   11.10 pm

2. 18:30   6.15 am

3. 23:10   10.25 am

4. 06:15   12.45 am

5. 00:45   6.30 pm

Write each time in the 24-hour clock time.

6. 4.30 pm ⟹ [.]

7. 6.25 am ⟹ [.]

8. 5.15 pm ⟹ [.]

9. 10.20 am ⟹ [.]

10. 11.55 pm ⟹ [.]

Colour in your score

Test 10 Data handling (1)

This **pictogram** shows information about 4 buses that make the same journey at different times.

Bus	Number of people on each bus
A	⭐ ⭐ ⭒
B	⭐ ⭐
C	⭐ ⭐ ⭐ ⭐ ⭐ ⭒
D	⭐ ⭐ ⭐

⭐ 5 people

⭒ 1 to 4 people

Passengers on bus C

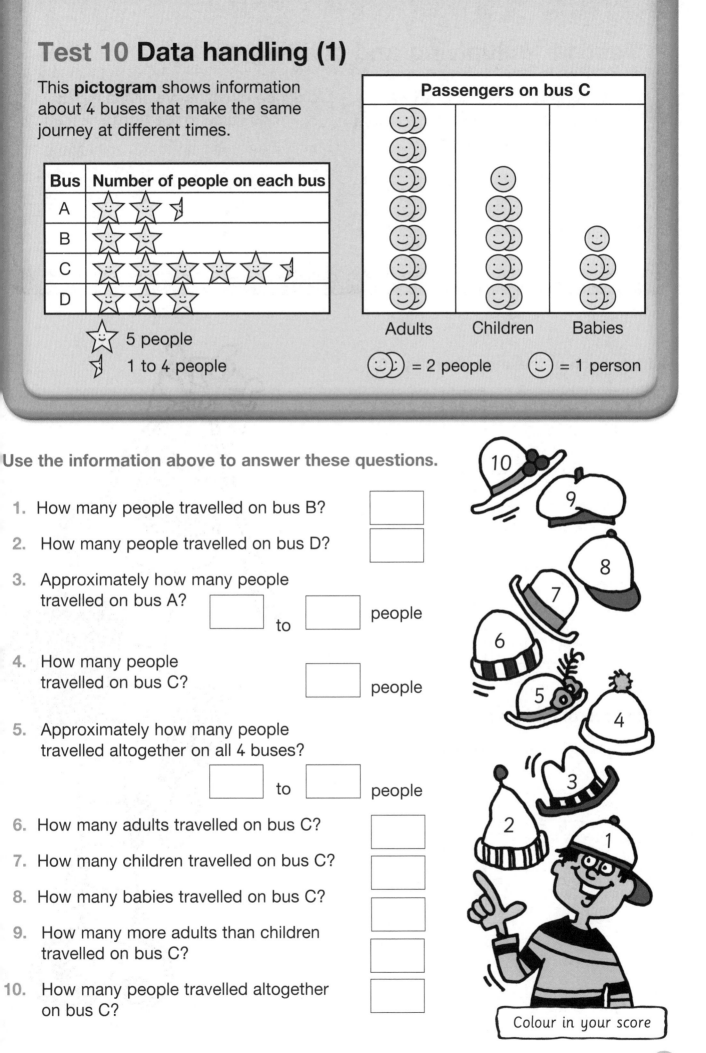

Adults   Children   Babies

😊😊 = 2 people   😊 = 1 person

Use the information above to answer these questions.

1. How many people travelled on bus B? ☐

2. How many people travelled on bus D? ☐

3. Approximately how many people travelled on bus A? ☐ to ☐ people

4. How many people travelled on bus C? ☐ people

5. Approximately how many people travelled altogether on all 4 buses? ☐ to ☐ people

6. How many adults travelled on bus C? ☐

7. How many children travelled on bus C? ☐

8. How many babies travelled on bus C? ☐

9. How many more adults than children travelled on bus C? ☐

10. How many people travelled altogether on bus C? ☐

Colour in your score

41

Test 11 Multiplying and dividing by 10

To **multiply by 10**, move all the digits to the **left**. The empty place is filled by a zero.

75 x 10 =

750

To **divide by 10**, move all the digits one place to the **right**.

230 ÷ 10 =

23

Multiply each of these numbers by 10.

1. | 45 | x 10 ⇒ |

2. | 63 | x 10 ⇒ |

3. | 81 | x 10 ⇒ |

4. | 107 | x 10 ⇒ |

5. | 234 | x 10 ⇒ |

Divide each of these numbers by 10.

6. | 53 | ÷10 ⇒ |

7. | 470 | ÷10 ⇒ |

8. | 380 | ÷10 ⇒ |

9. | 635 | ÷10 ⇒ |

10. | 8010 | ÷10 ⇒ |

Colour in your score

Test 12 **Addition**

Use mental methods to answer these.

1.   148 +   30 =

2.   36 +   323 =

3.   444 +   146 =

4.   138 +   700 =

5. 5610 +   29 =

6.   48 + 3037 =

7. 8100 +   763 =

8. 7210 +   490 =

9. 8139 + 1045 =

10. 1057 + 1074 =

Colour in your score

Test 13 Money: adding coins

When adding coins, start with the **highest value** coins to make it easier.

Write these totals using decimal notation.

1. £1   20p   20p   50p   2p   ⇨ ☐

2. £1   £1   20p   50p   10p   ⇨ ☐

3. 50p   20p   £2   2p   5p   ⇨ ☐

4. 10p   1p   2p   £2   £2   ⇨ ☐

5. 10p   50p   2p   5p   £1   ⇨ ☐

Which coins would you use to buy these books to give the exact money? Use the smallest possible number of coins.

6. £4.90 _____

7. £3.50 _____

8. £1.13 _____

9. £2.26 _____

10. £4.14 _____

Colour in your score

44

Test 14 **Measures problems**

When solving **measures problems**, make sure you read the questions carefully and then work out what calculations you need to do.

C 192 cm

D 240 cm

A 135 cm

B 155 cm

Use the information above to answer these questions.

1. What is the difference in length between the longest and shortest ropes? ▢ cm

2. How much longer is rope C than rope B? ▢ cm

3. What is the total length of ropes A and B? ▢ cm

4. Which rope is 85 cm longer than rope B? ▢

5. Which rope can be cut into 5 equal lengths of 27 cm? ▢

Work out the answers to these problems.

6. A chef has a 630 g bag of flour and uses 85 g. How much flour is left in the bag? ▢ g

7. Alex drove 5800 km in one year and 7600 km the following year. How much further did he drive in the second year? ▢ km

8. If 38 g of cake mixture is needed to make 1 cake, how much is needed to make 6 cakes? ▢ g

9. Vikram swam 850 m for a sponsored swim. He swam in widths of 10 m. How many widths did he swim? ▢

10. A pack of 6 cartons has 1260 ml of drinks in total. A can holds 240 ml. Which holds more, a can or a carton? ▢

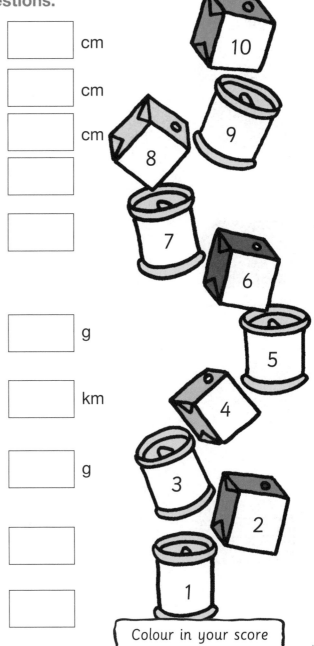

Colour in your score

10
9
8
7
6
5
4
3
2
1

Test 15 3-D shapes

These are the parts of a **3 dimensional** (3-D) shape.

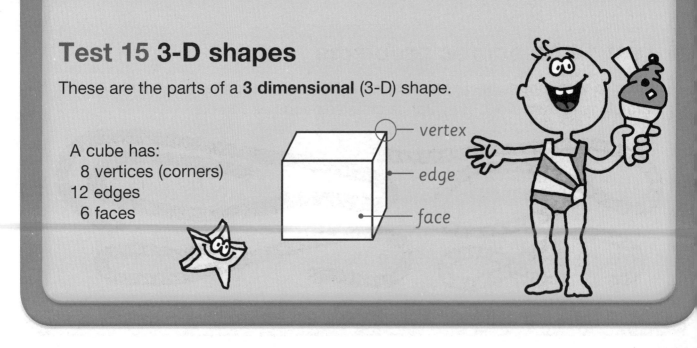

A cube has:
  8 vertices (corners)
  12 edges
  6 faces

vertex
edge
face

Name each shape. Write the missing numbers of corners, edges or faces.

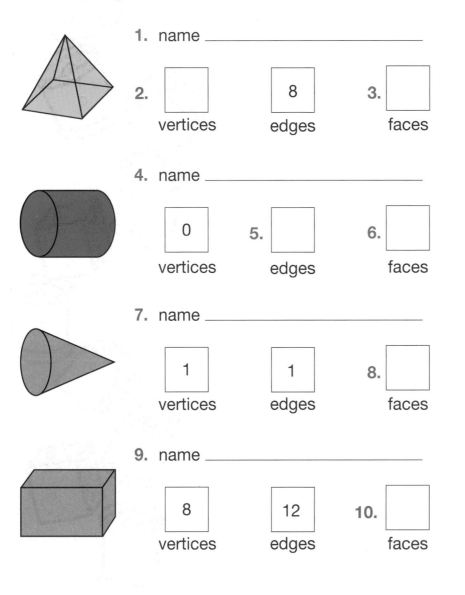

1. name _____

2. [ ] vertices   8 edges   3. [ ] faces

4. name _____

5. 0 vertices   5. [ ] edges   6. [ ] faces

7. name _____

1 vertices   1 edges   8. [ ] faces

9. name _____

8 vertices   12 edges   10. [ ] faces

10
9
8
7
6
5
4
3
2
1

Colour in your score

46

Test 16 Number patterns

Look for number patterns.

1	2	3	4	5	6
7	8	9	10	11	12
13	14	15	16	17	18
19	20	21	22	23	24
25	26	27	28	29	30
31	32	33	34	35	36

Write the next number in each number pattern.

1. 12 14 16 18 20 ☐

2. 15 18 21 24 27 ☐

3. 9 11 13 15 17 ☐

4. 33 30 27 24 21 ☐

5. 16 20 24 28 32 ☐

Write the missing number in each number pattern.

6. 22 20 18 ☐ 14 12 10

7. 27 24 ☐ 18 15 12 9

8. ☐ 28 30 32 34 36 38

9. 36 32 28 ☐ 20 16 12

10. 9 12 15 18 ☐ 24 27

Colour in your score

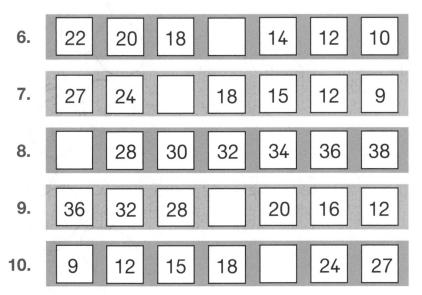

Test 17 **Division**

The box opposite shows one way to
divide 218 by 9.

		2	4	r	2	
9)	2	1	8			
−	1	8	0		→	(9 × 20)
		3	8			
	−	3	6		→	(9 × 4)
			2			remainder

**Work out these
division problems.**

1. 478 ÷ 5 = ⬚

2. 860 ÷ 7 = ⬚

3. 577 ÷ 4 = ⬚

4. 639 ÷ 9 = ⬚

5. 877 ÷ 6 = ⬚

Write the missing digit.

6.
```
      1  6 ⬚
   4) 6  7  6
```

7.
```
         7  7
   5) 3 ⬚ 5
```

8.
```
      ⬚  6
   6) 3  9  6
```

9.
```
      2  7  5
   3) ⬚ 2  5
```

10.
```
         3  1
   ⬚) 2  1  7
```

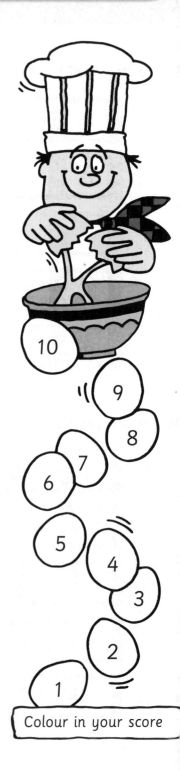

10

9

8

7

6

5

4

3

2

1

Colour in your score

48

Test 18 Money problems (1)

When finding the **difference** between two amounts, **count on** from the **lower** amount.

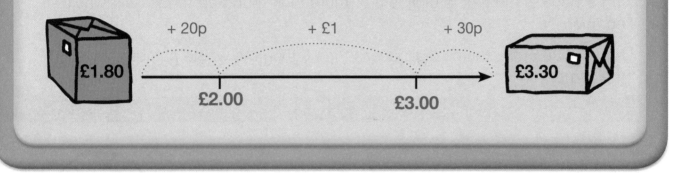

The **difference** between £1.80 and £3.30 is **£1.50** (20p + £1 + 30p).

Write the difference between these prices.

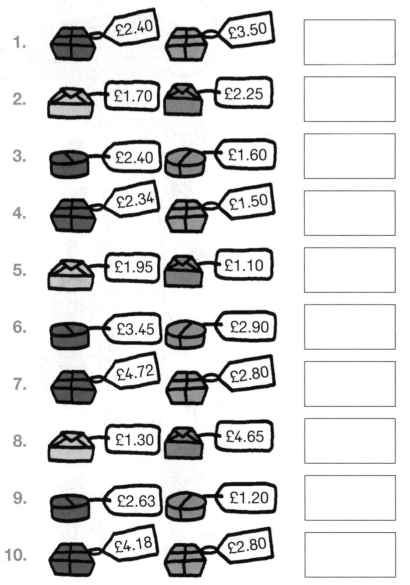

1. £2.40   £3.50

2. £1.70   £2.25

3. £2.40   £1.60

4. £2.34   £1.50

5. £1.95   £1.10

6. £3.45   £2.90

7. £4.72   £2.80

8. £1.30   £4.65

9. £2.63   £1.20

10. £4.18   £2.80

10
9
8
7
6
5
4
3
2
1

Colour in your score

49

Test 19 **Rounding decimals**

When rounding a decimal number to the nearest whole number look at the value of the tenths.

6.3 rounds **down** to 6

6.7 rounds **up** to 7

If the value of the tenths digit is 5 or more then round up to the next whole number.

If the value of the tenths digit is less than 5 then the whole number stays the same.

Write these numbers using decimals.

1. four point one six

2. fourteen point zero five

3. nought point two four

4. six and three hundredths

5. nine and nine tenths

Round these decimal numbers to the nearest whole number.

6. 5·6

7. 1·5

8. 0·6

9. 3·7

10. 4·2

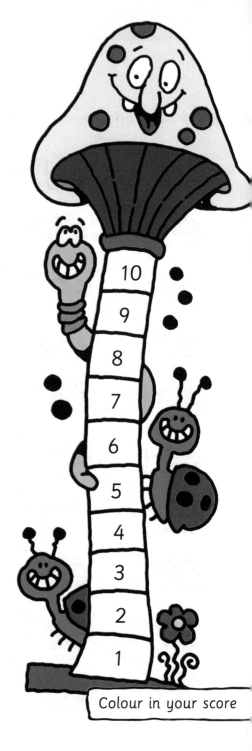

Colour in your score

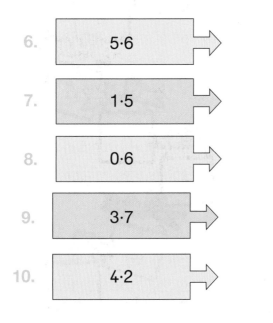

50

Test 20 Data handling (2)

The numbers 1-10 have been sorted on these two diagrams.

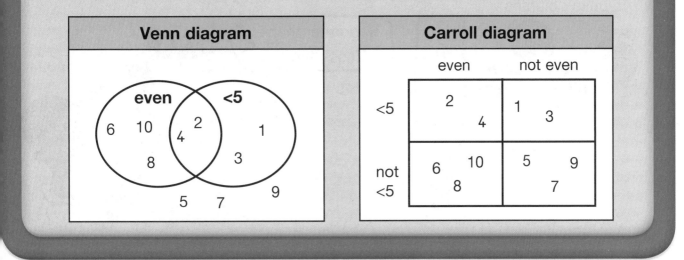

Venn diagram	Carroll diagram

Venn diagram

even <5
6 10
4 2
8
3
5 7
1
9

Carroll diagram

	even	not even
<5	2 4	1 3
not <5	6 10 8	5 9 7

Write the numbers in the correct place on each diagram.

> means greater than
< means less than

1. 7

2. 31

3. 28

4. 16

5. 19

odd >20

6. 24

7. 13

8. 15

9. 1

10. 6

	even	not even
<10		
not <10		

Colour in your score

Test 21 Place value (2)

To help work out the **order of numbers**, you can write them in a list, lining up the units columns.

Write the signs > or < for each pair of numbers.

1. 6093 ☐ 6103

2. 4206 ☐ 4311

3. 7415 ☐ 7409

4. 2046 ☐ 2050

5. 8114 ☐ 8108

Write the numbers in order starting with the smallest.

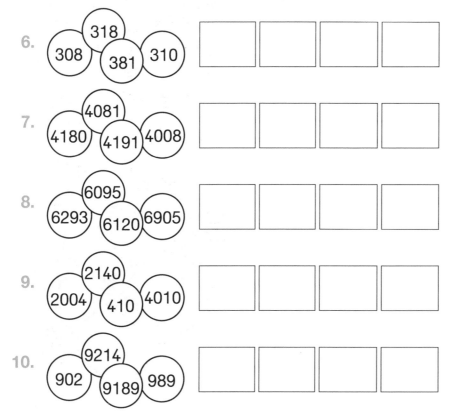

6. 318 308 381 310 ☐ ☐ ☐ ☐

7. 4081 4180 4191 4008 ☐ ☐ ☐ ☐

8. 6095 6293 6120 6905 ☐ ☐ ☐ ☐

9. 2140 2004 410 4010 ☐ ☐ ☐ ☐

10. 9214 902 9189 989 ☐ ☐ ☐ ☐

Colour in your score

52

Test 22 Addition and subtraction (2)

Some questions are easier to work out in your head than writing them down.

It is quicker to answer 386 – 99 mentally than as a written calculation.

See which of these you can answer in your head.

1. Total 437 and 59.

2. Take 66 away from 385.

3. 3765 add 200.

4. 5793 subtract 50.

5. Increase 472 by 84.

Write the missing numbers.

6.   3·7   +   =   5

7.   3   –   =   1·5

8.   125   +   =   500

9. 1000   –   =   225

10.   +   550   = 1000

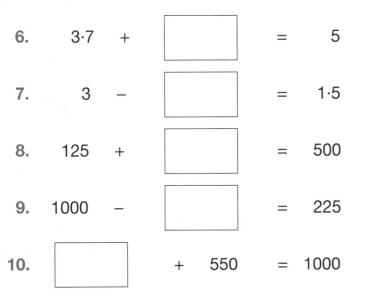

Colour in your score

Test 23 **Perimeter**

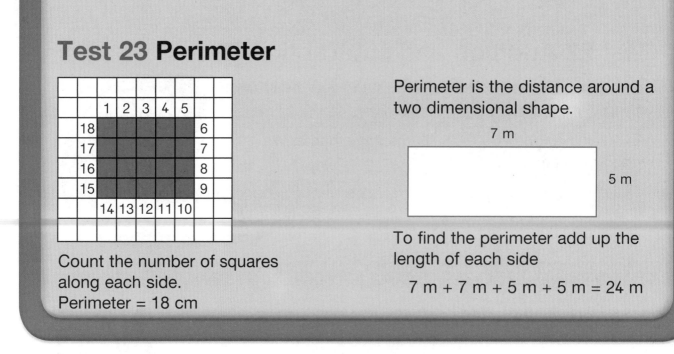

Count the number of squares along each side.
Perimeter = 18 cm

Perimeter is the distance around a two dimensional shape.

To find the perimeter add up the length of each side

7 m + 7 m + 5 m + 5 m = 24 m

Find the perimeter of each of these shapes, in squares.

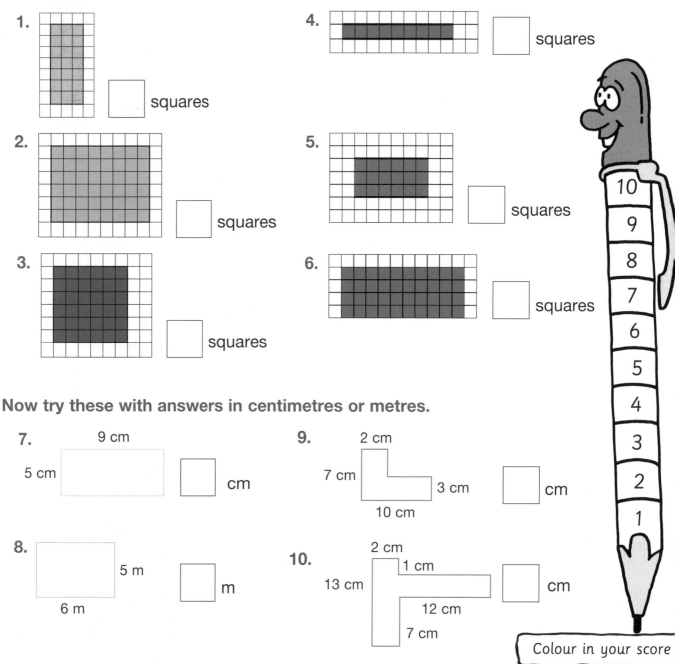

1. ☐ squares

2. ☐ squares

3. ☐ squares

4. ☐ squares

5. ☐ squares

6. ☐ squares

Now try these with answers in centimetres or metres.

7. 9 cm / 5 cm / ☐ cm

8. 5 m / 6 m / ☐ m

9. 2 cm / 7 cm / 3 cm / 10 cm / ☐ cm

10. 2 cm / 1 cm / 13 cm / 12 cm / 7 cm / ☐ cm

10 9 8 7 6 5 4 3 2 1

Colour in your score

Test 24 Shape: symmetry

A shape has line **symmetry** if both sides are exactly the same when a mirror line is drawn.

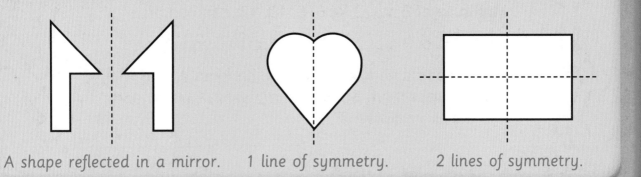

A shape reflected in a mirror.   1 line of symmetry.   2 lines of symmetry.

Draw the reflection of each shape.

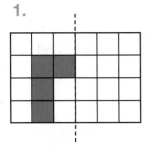

1.   2.   3.

4.   5.

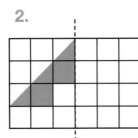
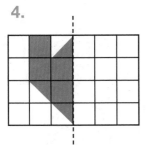
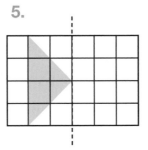

Draw the lines of symmetry on each shape.

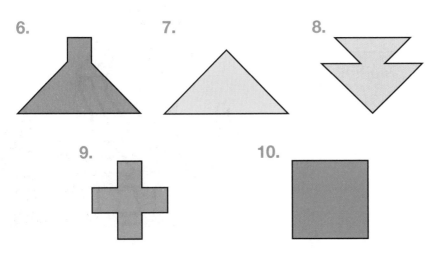

6.   7.   8.

9.   10.

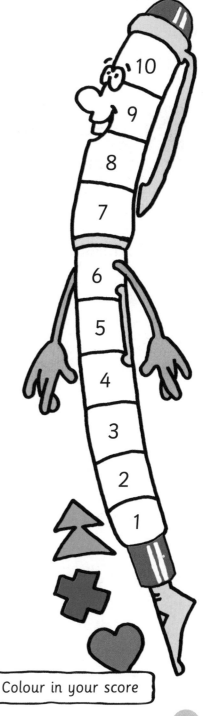

Colour in your score

55

Test 25 **Multiples**

Multiples of 2 are: 2, 4, 6, 8, 10, 12... and so on.

Multiples of 3 are: 3, 6, 9, 12, 15, 18... and so on.

Multiples of a number do not come to an end at ×12, they go on and on. So, for example, 82, 94, 106 and 300 are all multiples of 2.

Which of these numbers are multiples of 2, 3, 4 or 5?
Some numbers are used more than once.

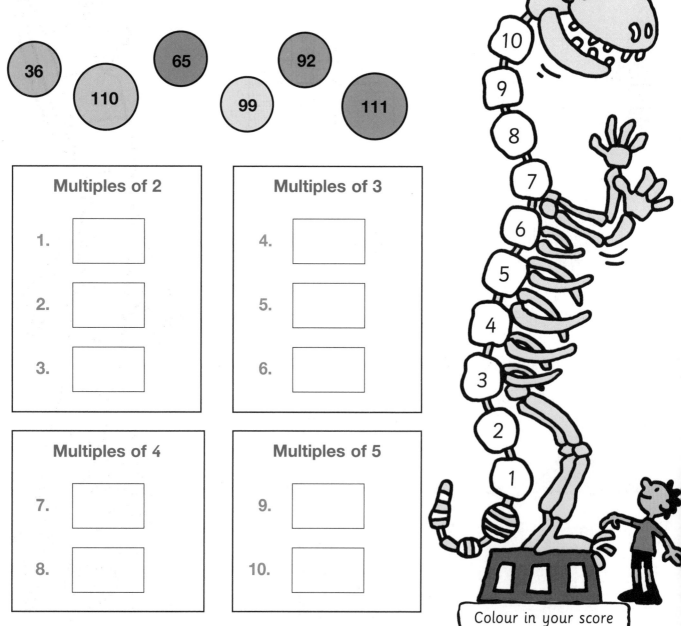

36   110   65   99   92   111

Multiples of 2

1.
2.
3.

Multiples of 3

4.
5.
6.

Multiples of 4

7.
8.

Multiples of 5

9.
10.

10
9
8
7
6
5
4
3
2
1

Colour in your score

Test 26 **Multiplication and division**

The opposite, or inverse, of multiplication is division.

$24 \times 3 = 72$ so $72 \div 3 = 24$

The opposite, or inverse, of division is multiplication.

$75 \div 5 = 15$ so $15 \times 5 = 75$

Complete the number machine tables.

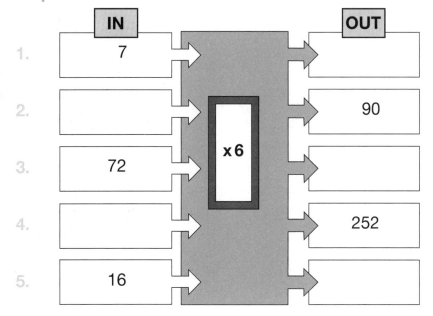

	IN		OUT
1.	7		
2.		×6	90
3.	72		
4.			252
5.	16		

Write the missing numbers.

6. 40 × ☐ = 240

7. 800 ÷ ☐ = 40

8. 30 × ☐ = 1500

9. 60 ÷ ☐ = 2

10. 50 × ☐ = 450

Colour in your score

57

When working out **word problems**, read the questions carefully to work out the calculations you need to do.

Answer these problems.

1. Amy has 95p and spends 57p. How much money does she have left?

2. A cinema ticket costs £3.50 for an adult and £3 for a child. What is the total cost for 2 adults and 2 children?

3. A newspaper costs 35p. What is the cost for a week's supply of newspapers?

4. A sweet costs 14p. How many can be bought for £1?

5. A bus journey costs £1.20. How much will the total fare be for 4 people?

6. A car costs £2400. If it is reduced by £800, how much will it cost?

7. A book costs £4.70. It is reduced by £1.90 in a sale. What is the new price of the book?

8. Sam has two 20p coins and a 50p coin. He buys a magazine at 72p. How much money does he have left?

9. What is the total cost of a £4.50 T-shirt and a £3.70 pair of shorts?

10. If a fairground ride costs 80p, what is the cost of 3 rides?

Colour in your score

58

Test 28 **Decimals**

hundreds		tens		ones	(decimal point)	tenths		hundredths
2		4		3	•	2		5
200	+	40	+	3	+	$\frac{2}{10}$	+	$\frac{5}{100}$

Write in words the value of the bold digits in these numbers.

1. 3**5**·3

2. 274·**2**1

3. 0·**37**

4. **2**7·3

5. 462·**9**

Write the number each arrow points to.

6.

```
0        0·1        0·2        0·3        0·4        0·5
├┼┼┼┼┼┼┼┼┼┼┼┼┼┼┼┼┼┼┼┼┼┼┼┼┼┼┼┼┼┼┼┼┼┼┼┼┼┼┼┼┤
```

7.

```
0        0·1        0·2        0·3        0·4        0·5
├┼┼┼┼┼┼┼┼┼┼┼┼┼┼┼┼┼┼┼┼┼┼┼┼┼┼┼┼┼┼┼┼┼┼┼┼┼┼┼┼┤
```

8.

```
0        0·1        0·2        0·3        0·4        0·5
├┼┼┼┼┼┼┼┼┼┼┼┼┼┼┼┼┼┼┼┼┼┼┼┼┼┼┼┼┼┼┼┼┼┼┼┼┼┼┼┼┤
```

9.

```
0   0·1   0·2   0·3   0·4   0·5   0·6   0·7   0·8   0·9   1
├┼┼┼┼┼┼┼┼┼┼┼┼┼┼┼┼┼┼┼┼┼┼┼┼┼┼┼┼┼┼┼┼┼┼┼┼┼┼┼┼┤
```

10.

```
0   0·1   0·2   0·3   0·4   0·5   0·6   0·7   0·8   0·9   1
├┼┼┼┼┼┼┼┼┼┼┼┼┼┼┼┼┼┼┼┼┼┼┼┼┼┼┼┼┼┼┼┼┼┼┼┼┼┼┼┼┤
```

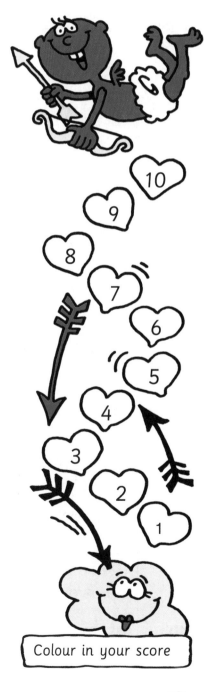

10
9
8
7
6
5
4
3
2
1

Colour in your score

Test 29 Time problems

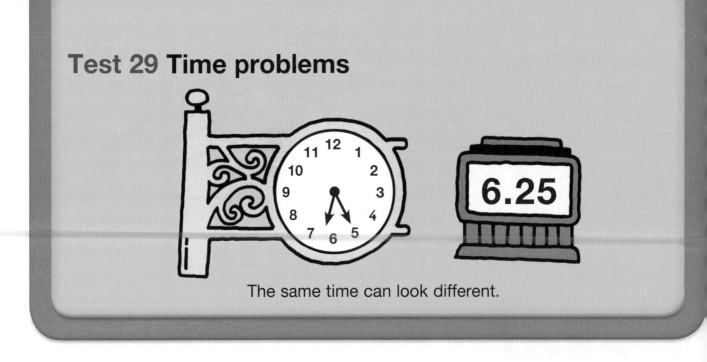

The same time can look different.

These clocks are 45 minutes fast.
Write the real time for each of them.

1.

4.

2.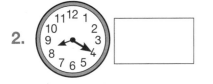

5.

3.

A train takes 20 minutes between each of these stations.
Complete the timetable.

6.	Smedley	2.10	
7.	Chadwick		4.45
8.	Welby	2.50	
9.	Burnsford		5.25
10.	Ragby		5.45

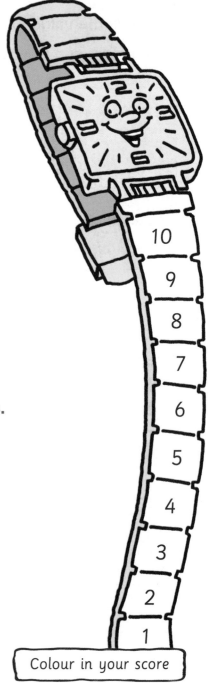

10

9

8

7

6

5

4

3

2

1

Colour in your score

60

Test 30 Data handling (3)

These **graphs** show the number of cans collected by two classes in a school over a month.

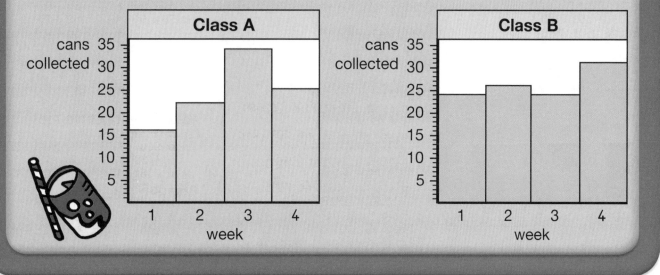

Answer these problems.

1. How many cans were collected by Class A in week 2?

2. How many cans were collected by Class B in week 1?

3. In which week did Class A collect 25 cans?

4. How many more cans were collected in week 1 by Class B than by Class A?

5. In which week did Class A collect 10 more cans than Class B?

6. In which week did Class B collect 26 cans?

7. In which 2 weeks were the same number of cans collected by Class B?

8. How many fewer cans were collected in week 4 by Class A than Class B?

9. How many cans altogether were collected by Class B?

10. Which class collected the most cans?

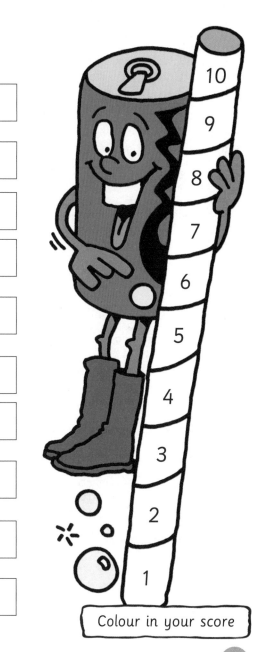

Colour in your score

ANSWERS

Page 2
1. a 758, 759, 760
   b 618, 608, 598
   c 506, 516, 526
   d 1641, 2641, 3641
   e 285, 185, 85
   f 8030, 7030, 6030
2.

¹7	²4	3			⁷9	
³3	■	0	■	⁴6	6	
5	■	⁵9	2	0	0	
1			⁶8	0	7	4

Page 3
The missing numbers are:
1. a 50, 125, 150, 175   rule +25
   b 24, 30, 36, 48   rule +6
   c 9, 27, 54, 63   rule +9
   d 21, 42, 49, 56   rule +7
   e 3000, 4000, 5000,   rule +1000
   7000
   f 54, 60, 72, 90   rule +6

2. a −4, −3, −1, 1, 2
   b −3, −2, −1, 2, 3
   c −7, −6, −5, −3, −1, 0
   d −2, −1, 0, 1, 2, 4

Page 4
1. a 5 tens   g 9 ones
   b 6 thousands   h 7 hundreds
   c 8 ones   i 3 tens
   d 2 hundreds   j 4 ones
   e 6 tens   k 8 thousands
   f 5 thousands   l 7 hundreds

2. a 400   f 5000
   b 800   g 3000
   c 400   h 3000
   d 400   i 5000
   e 500   j 9000

Page 5
1. a 54 and 86   d 229
   b 540   e 124 and 86
   c 154   f 419

2. a 8262   e £46.44
   b 11923   f £136.05
   c 6063   g £48.75
   d 9025   h £66.40

Page 6
1. a triangle ✔   g quadrilateral
   b octagon ✔   h pentagon ✔
   c pentagon   i hexagon ✔
   d octagon   j decagon
   e heptagon   k nonagon
   f hexagon   l triangle

2. For a, b, c, d and h, there are
   many possible answers. Check
   each shape has the correct
   number of sides.
   d Check there is a right angle.
   e

f

g

Page 7
1. a £958, £1090, £1900, £2589,
   £2850
   b 965 km, 2830 km, 3095 km,
   3520 km, 3755 km
   c 1599 g, 1995 g, 2046 g,
   2460 g, 2604 g
   d 4599 ml, 4600 ml, 7025 ml,
   7028 ml, 7529 ml

2. 2389, 2398, 2839, 2893, 2938,
   2983
   3289, 3298, 3829, 3892, 3928,
   3982
   8239, 8293, 8329, 8392, 8923,
   8932
   9238, 9283, 9328, 9382, 9823,
   9832

Page 8
1. a

b 6:20 → 8:40

c

d 1:45 → 3:15

2. a 15 minutes   d 15 minutes
   b 25 minutes   e 20 minutes
   c 5 minutes   f 25 minutes

Page 9
1. a $\frac{8}{10} = \frac{4}{5}$ f 9
   b $\frac{4}{12} = \frac{1}{3}$ g 5
   c $\frac{6}{8} = \frac{3}{4}$ h 5
   d $\frac{9}{15} = \frac{3}{5}$ i 18
   e 2   j 4

2. a $\frac{1}{10}$, $\frac{2}{10}$, $\frac{1}{4}$, $\frac{1}{2}$, $\frac{3}{5}$, $\frac{2}{3}$, $\frac{3}{4}$, $\frac{9}{10}$

Page 10
1. a 3500 m   f 6.5 or $6\frac{1}{2}$ km
   b 4 cm   g 220 mm
   c 1.5 or $1\frac{1}{2}$ m   h 18 000 m
   d 80 mm   i 475 cm
   e 25 cm   j 6.5 or $6\frac{1}{2}$ cm

2. a 45 mm   d 37 mm
   b 62 mm   e 71 mm
   c 58 mm

Page 11
1. a $3 \times 8 = 24$ c 6
   $8 \times 3 = 24$ d 21
   $24 \div 3 = 8$ e 6
   $24 \div 8 = 3$ f 12
   b $7 \times 4 = 28$ g 4
   $4 \times 7 = 28$ h 5
   $28 \div 4 = 7$ i 77
   $28 \div 7 = 4$ j 8

2. $60 \div 9 \rightarrow 6$ $37 \div 3 \rightarrow 1$
   $93 \div 10 \rightarrow 3$ $48 \div 5 \rightarrow 3$

$89 \div 5 \rightarrow 4$ $65 \div 6 \rightarrow 5$
$38 \div 6 \rightarrow 2$ $80 \div 3 \rightarrow 2$
$106 \div 10 \rightarrow 6$ $53 \div 6 \rightarrow 5$
$61 \div 2 \rightarrow 1$ $46 \div 6 \rightarrow 4$

Page 12
1. a >   d <   g >   j >
   b <   e >   h <   k <
   c >   f >   i <   l >

2. a 4168, 4167, 4166, 4165
   b 3839, 3840, 3841
   c 9001, 9000, 8999, 8998, 8997
   d 4422, 4423, 4424, 4425
   e 7081, 7080, 7079, 7078, 7077

Page 13
1. a cuboid   d sphere
   b cylinder   e cube
   c cone   f (square-based)
   pyramid

2.	faces	edges	vertices
a	5	8	5
b	6	12	8
c	5	9	6
d	4	6	4

Page 14
1. a 2 kg   g 10 000 g
   b 1500 g   h 6.75 or $6\frac{3}{4}$ kg
   c 5.5 or $5\frac{1}{2}$ kg   i 2500 g
   d 1.25 or $1\frac{1}{4}$ kg   j 4750 g
   e 7000 g   k 9.5 or $9\frac{1}{2}$ kg
   f 3250 g   l 1750 g

2. a 1.5 or $1\frac{1}{2}$ kg   d 650 g
   b 2.5 or $2\frac{1}{2}$ kg   e 1700 g
   c 0.5 or $\frac{1}{2}$ kg   f 600 g

Page 15
1. a 183   d 688   g 252
   b 77   e 968   h 1387
   c 369   f 173

2. These are possible answers
   a $9876 − 2345 = 7531$
   b $6234 − 5987 = 247$
   c $4935 − 2876 = 2059$ or $4876 - 2935 = 1941$

Page 16
1. a 36 squares
   b 30 squares
   c 20 squares

2. Rectangles with the dimensions
   2×4 and 1×8.

Page 17
1. a 228   e 1314
   b 378   f 2268
   c 765   g 2048
   d 512   h 1420

2. a 189   f 691
   b 130 r 4   g 696
   c 181 r 2   h 438
   d 80 r 5   i 358
   e 602

Page 18
1. a   d

b 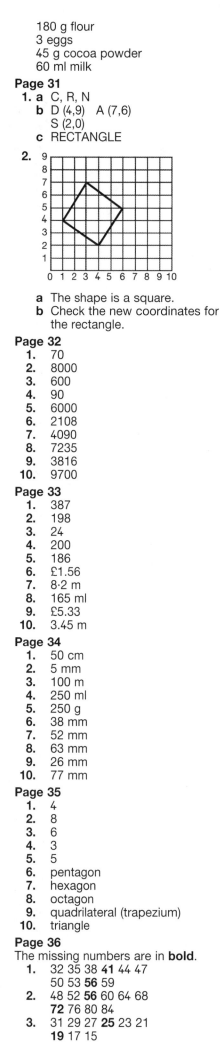 **e**

c **f**

2. a **d**

2 lines of symmetry   4 lines of symmetry

b **e**

3 lines of symmetry   5 lines of symmetry

c

6 lines of symmetry

Page 19
1. a 3 l
  b 1500 ml
  c 6000 ml
  d 2.25 or $2\frac{1}{4}$ l
  e 1.75 or $1\frac{3}{4}$ l
  f 10 000 ml
  g 3500 ml
  h 2 l
  i 4.5 or $4\frac{1}{2}$ l
  j 8750 ml
  k 5.75 or $5\frac{3}{4}$ l
  l 6750 ml

2. a 500 ml
  b 750 ml
  c 100 ml
  d 250 ml
  e 1000 ml
  f 300 ml
  g 500 ml
  h 1500 ml

Page 20
1. a 0.3
  b 0.5
  c 0.2
  d 0.75
  e 0.17
  f 0.4
  g 0.41
  h 0.9
  i 0.65
  j 0.5
  k 0.59
  l 0.25

2. a 0.2, 0.4, 0.6, 0.7, 0.9
  b 3.1, 3.4, 3.6, 3.7, 3.9
  c 6.12, 6.14, 6.15, 6.17, 6.18

Page 21
1. a silver
  b 12
  c 10
  d blue
  e 9
  f 106

2. a 45
  b Thursday
  c 6
  d Wednesday

Page 22
1. a red
  b blue
  c yellow
  d red
  e blue
  f red
  g blue
  h yellow
  i yellow

2.

Isosceles   Right-angled

e   c a f   b g
   d
h

Page 23
1. a $\frac{4}{6} = \frac{2}{3}$
  b $\frac{6}{10} = \frac{3}{5}$
  c $\frac{4}{8} = \frac{1}{2}$
  d $\frac{6}{8} = \frac{3}{4}$
  e 4
  f 3
  g 5
  h 5
  i 12
  j 3

2. a $\frac{7}{15}$ **b** $\frac{5}{25}$ **c** $\frac{8}{27}$

Page 24

1.

Total drop (m)	Nearest 10 m	Nearest 100 m
979	980	1000
947	950	900
774	770	800
739	740	700
646	650	600
581	580	600
561	560	600

2. a 160
  b 200
  c 100
  d 800
  e 1100
  f 200

Page 25
1. Multiples of 2 – 48, 56, 100, 86, 52, 82, 42, 70, 60
Multiples of 6 – 48, 42, 60
Multiples of 4 – 48, 56, 100, 52, 60
Multiples of 5 – 100, 85, 70, 115, 60, 65

2. You can see these patterns:
The red squares make diagonal lines and the blue squares make two vertical lines.
The ones digits in the numbers on each blue line are the same: 5s or 0s.
Starting at the top of each red line, the tens digits ascend, while the ones digits descend, e.g. the first line is 3, 12, 21: tens digits (0), 1, 2; ones digits 3, 2, 1.

Page 26
1. a £1.75
  b £1.35
  c £1.44
  d £1.45
  e 28p
  f 76p

2. a £6.51
  b £1.01
  c £2.11
  d £6.31
  e £2.41
  f £1.11
  g £2.61
  h £3.41

Page 27
1. a

obtuse

b

acute

c

acute

d

obtuse

2. a East
  b East
  c South-west
  d East
  e South-east
  f West

Page 28
1. a 07:30
  b 21:00
  c 10:15
  d 16:45
  e 02:10
  f 23:50
  g 9.30 am
  h 3.00 pm
  i 8.15 pm
  j 1.40 pm
  k 10.55 am
  l 10.20 pm

2. a 4 h 15 minutes
  b 3 h 40 minutes
  c 2 h 50 minutes
  d 50 minutes

Page 29
1. a 26
  b Tuesday
  c 17
  d Monday
  e Graph should read 35 books
  f 145

2. Check child's graph

Page 30
1. a £1.80
  b 55 g
  c £5.90
  d 7
  e 10
  f £16.50
  g 240 km
  h 17

2. 150 g margarine
120 g sugar
180 g flour
3 eggs
45 g cocoa powder
60 ml milk

Page 31
1. a C, R, N
  b D (4,9)   A (7,6)
     S (2,0)
  c RECTANGLE

2.

a The shape is a square.
b Check the new coordinates for the rectangle.

Page 32
  1. 70
  2. 8000
  3. 600
  4. 90
  5. 6000
  6. 2108
  7. 4090
  8. 7235
  9. 3816
  10. 9700

Page 33
  1. 387
  2. 198
  3. 24
  4. 200
  5. 186
  6. £1.56
  7. 8·2 m
  8. 165 ml
  9. £5.33
  10. 3.45 m

Page 34
  1. 50 cm
  2. 5 mm
  3. 100 m
  4. 250 ml
  5. 250 g
  6. 38 mm
  7. 52 mm
  8. 63 mm
  9. 26 mm
  10. 77 mm

Page 35
  1. 4
  2. 8
  3. 6
  4. 3
  5. 5
  6. pentagon
  7. hexagon
  8. octagon
  9. quadrilateral (trapezium)
  10. triangle

Page 36
The missing numbers are in **bold**.
  1. 32 35 38 **41** 44 47 50 53 **56** 59
  2. 48 52 **56** 60 64 68 **72** 76 80 84
  3. 31 29 27 **25** 23 21 **19** 17 15

4. 230 210 **190** 170 150 **130** 110 90 70

5. 76 81 86 91 **96** 101 106 **111** 116

6. −2
7. 4
8. −7
9. −3
10. −1

Page 37
1. 5   **6.** 5
2. 11   **7.** 66
3. 24   **8.** 9
4. 4   **9.** 12
5. 5   **10.** 9

Page 38
1. 235p   **6.** 275p
2. 645p   **7.** £2.55
3. £3.70   **8.** £3.15
4. 109p   **9.** £4.05
5. £2.14   **10.** £4.10

Page 39
1. $\frac{4}{10} = \frac{2}{5}$
2. $\frac{3}{6} = \frac{1}{2}$
3. $\frac{2}{8} = \frac{1}{4}$
4. $\frac{6}{8} = \frac{3}{4}$
5. $\frac{4}{8} = \frac{1}{2}$
6. $\frac{8}{10}$
7. $\frac{6}{9}$
8. $\frac{1}{4}$
9. $\frac{9}{12}$
10. $\frac{6}{20}$

Page 40
1. 10.25am
2. 6.30pm
3. 11.10pm
4. 6.15am
5. 12.45am
6. 16:30
7. 06:25
8. 17:15
9. 10:20
10. 23:55

Page 41
1. 10
2. 15
3. 11 to 14 people
4. 28 people
5. 62 to 68 people
6. 14
7. 9
8. 5
9. 5
10. 28

Page 42
1. 450
2. 630
3. 810
4. 1070
5. 2340
6. 5.3
7. 47
8. 38
9. 63.5
10. 801

Page 43
1. 178
2. 359
3. 590

4. 838
5. 5639
6. 3085
7. 8863
8. 7700
9. 9184
10. 2131

Page 44
1. £1.92
2. £2.80
3. £2.77
4. £4.13
5. £1.67
6. £2 £2 50p 20p 20p
7. £2 £1 50p
8. £1 10p 2p 1p
9. £2 20p 5p 1p
10. £2 £2 10p 2p 2p

Page 45
1. 105 cm
2. 37 cm
3. 290 cm
4. D
5. A
6. 545 g
7. 1800 km
8. 228 g
9. 85
10. can

Page 46
1. (square-based) pyramid
2. 5 corners
3. 5 faces
4. cylinder
5. 2 edges
6. 3 faces
7. cone
8. 2 faces
9. cuboid
10. 6 faces

Page 47
1. 22   **6.** 16
2. 30   **7.** 21
3. 19   **8.** 26
4. 18   **9.** 24
5. 36   **10.** 21

Page 48
1. 95 remainder 3
2. 122 remainder 6
3. 144 remainder 1
4. 71
5. 146 remainder 1
6. 9
7. 8
8. 6
9. 8
10. 7

Page 49
1. £1.10   **6.** 55p
2. 55p   **7.** £1.92
3. 80p   **8.** £3.35
4. 84p   **9.** £1.43
5. 85p   **10.** £1.38

Page 50
1. 4·16
2. 14·05
3. 0·24
4. 6·03
5. 9·9
6. 6
7. 2
8. 1

9. 4
10. 4

Page 51
1–5.

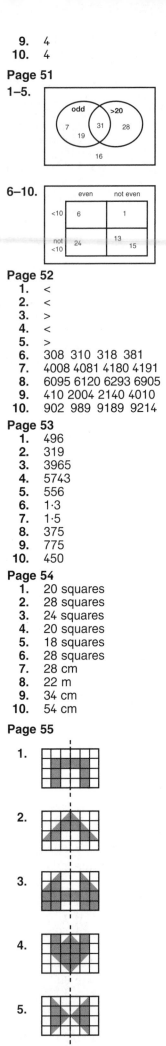

6–10.

	even	not even
<10	6	1
not <10	24	13 15

Page 52
1. <
2. <
3. >
4. <
5. >
6. 308 310 318 381
7. 4008 4081 4180 4191
8. 6095 6120 6293 6905
9. 410 2004 2140 4010
10. 902 989 9189 9214

Page 53
1. 496
2. 319
3. 3965
4. 5743
5. 556
6. 1·3
7. 1·5
8. 375
9. 775
10. 450

Page 54
1. 20 squares
2. 28 squares
3. 24 squares
4. 20 squares
5. 18 squares
6. 28 squares
7. 28 cm
8. 22 m
9. 34 cm
10. 54 cm

Page 55
1.
2.
3.
4.
5.

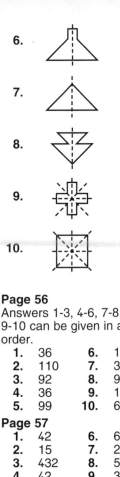

6.
7.
8.
9.
10.

Page 56
Answers 1-3, 4-6, 7-8 and 9-10 can be given in any order.
1. 36   **6.** 111
2. 110   **7.** 36
3. 92   **8.** 92
4. 36   **9.** 110
5. 99   **10.** 65

Page 57
1. 42   **6.** 6
2. 15   **7.** 20
3. 432   **8.** 50
4. 42   **9.** 30
5. 96   **10.** 9

Page 58
1. 38p
2. £13
3. £2.45
4. 7
5. £4.80
6. £1600
7. £2.80
8. 18p
9. £8.20
10. £2.40

Page 59
1. five
2. one hundredth
3. three tenths
4. twenty
5. nine tenths
6. 0·09
7. 0·45
8. 0·33
9. 0·22
10. 0·05

Page 60
1. 3.45   **6.** 4.25
2. 7.35   **7.** 2.30
3. 1.25   **8.** 5.05
4. 6.30   **9.** 3.10
5. 10.50   **10.** 3.30

Page 61
1. 22
2. 24
3. 4
4. 8
5. 3
6. 2
7. weeks 1 and 3
8. 6
9. 105
10. B

English

Age 8-9

Contents

Activities

Quick Tests

Alison Head and Louis Fidge

Speaking and listening (1)

Interviewing someone is a great way to see if you can listen carefully and remember what was said – it's fun, too!

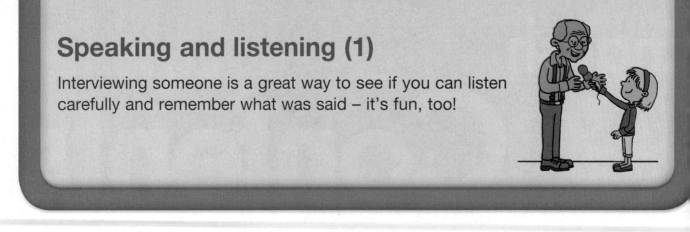

1 Interview a relative who is older than you about what it was like when they went to school. Plan some questions to ask them, using the words in the box to help you.

a _____

b _____

c _____

d _____

e _____

> lunchtime
>
> games
>
> assembly
>
> homework
>
> lessons
>
> PE
>
> teachers
>
> uniform

2 Can you remember what they said? Write an account of what you remember below. Was their school very similar or different to your experiences?

_____

_____

_____

_____

_____

_____

_____

_____

_____

_____

_____

Homophones

Homophones are words that **sound the same**, but have **different meanings** or **spellings**.

You need to think about the whole sentence to know which is the right word to use.

flour   flower

We bought some **flour** to bake the cake.

I picked a red **flower**.

1 Write homophones for these words.

a knew   _____

b hole   _____

c grate   _____

d there   _____

e two   _____

f herd   _____

g sea   _____

h be   _____

i for   _____

j write   _____

2 Write a sentence for each word to show you know how to use it correctly.

a plaice   _We had plaice and chips._____

b place   _I know the place you mean._____

c threw   _____

d through _____

e son   _____

f sun   _____

g floor   _____

h flaw   _____

i main   _____

j mane   _____

Verb endings

Verbs tell us what a person or thing is **doing**. The ending of the verb changes depending on **who** is doing the activity and whether it has already happened (past), is happening now (present) or will happen (future).

she walk**ed**   she walk**s**   she will be walk**ing**

Sometimes the spelling of the verb changes when the ending is added.

1 Complete the rows by adding the correct ending to each verb.

	s	ed	ing
a jump	jumps	jumped	_____
b prefer	prefers	_____	preferring
c kick	_____	kicked	kicking
d grab	grabs	_____	grabbing
e garden	gardens	gardened	_____
f save	saves	_____	_____
g lift	_____	lifted	_____

2 Rewrite these sentences, using the correct form of the verb in bold.

a The car **stops** a few seconds ago at the traffic lights.

_____

b Yesterday Dad **limit** the number of chips he ate.

_____

c I **carrying** the shopping home for Gran yesterday.

_____

d Mum always **washing** the car on Saturdays after we go swimming.

_____

e It **beginning** to rain last night.

_____

f Jenny always **exploring** the rock pools as soon as she gets to the beach.

_____

Suffixes *ship*, *ness* and *ment*

We can add suffixes to the **ends** of some words to change their meaning.

Ship, ness and *ment* are suffixes which do not change the spelling of the root word.

sponsor + **ship** = sponsorship

fair + **ness** = fairness

battle + **ment** = battlement

The only exception is if the word ends in a consonant followed by *y*, when you change the *y* to *i* before adding the suffix.

tidy + **ness** = tidiness

1 Complete these word sums.

a merry + ment = _____

b kind + ness = _____

c fit + ness = _____

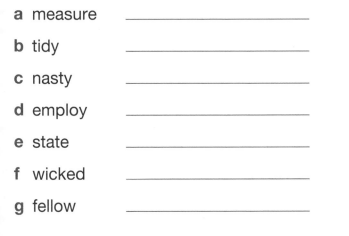

d enjoy + ment = _____

e lazy + ness = _____

f member + ship = _____

g silly + ness = _____

h friend + ship = _____

i careless + ness = _____

j happy + ness = _____

2 Choose *ship*, *ness* or *ment* to add to each of these words. Then write down the new word.

a measure _____

b tidy _____

c nasty _____

d employ _____

e state _____

f wicked _____

g fellow _____

h apprentice _____

i replace _____

j champion _____

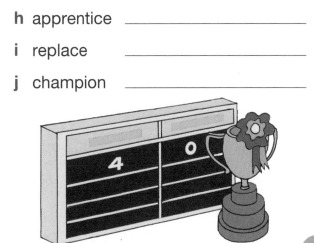

Speaking and listening (2)

Giving spoken or oral reports is a great way to practise speaking clearly and confidently. Spoken reviews are another good way to make sure you can organise ideas, and report them orally.

1 Give a spoken review of your favourite film to a grown-up.

a What is the title of your favourite film?

_____

b Who is your favourite character, and why?

_____

c What, in your opinion, is the most exciting thing that happens in the film?

_____

d How do you feel about the ending? Does it resolve any problems that arose during the story?

_____

2 Make notes to help you plan a spoken report about an exciting day out.

a Where did you go, and why?

_____

b What transport did you use to get there? Was it far? How long did it take?

_____

c Describe what happened during the day.

_____

d Would you want to go again if you got the chance? Give reasons for your answer.

_____

e Would you recommend the day out to a friend?

_____

Alphabetical order

Putting words in alphabetical order helps us to find information in **dictionaries** and **indexes**.

If the first two letters of a group of words are the same, we can use the third and fourth letters to put the words in alphabetical order.

baby   baggage   ball

a **b** c d e f **g** h i j k **l** m n o p q r s t u v w x y z

Use the third bold letter to find each word in the box. Then write the missing letters so the words are in alphabetical order. The first one has been done for you.

sunny   super   suspect   submarine   sudden
summer   sugar   suitable   success

a su**b**marine

b su**c**_____

c su**d**_____

d su**g**_____

e su**i**_____

f su**m**_____

g su**n**_____

h su**p**_____

i su**s**_____

Write these words in alphabetical order, using the third and fourth letters.

hair   hare   hat   hail
harp   hard   haste   have

a _____   e _____

b _____   f _____

c _____   g _____

d _____   h _____

Adverbs

Adverbs tell us **how** a person or thing does something.

I walked **quickly** to school.

The fish swam **energetically**.

1 Complete the word sums to spell these adverbs correctly.

a complete + ly = _____

b comic + ly = _____

c usual + ly = _____

d sleepy + ly = _____

e bad + ly = _____

f total + ly = _____

g humble + ly = _____

h basic + ly = _____

i gentle + ly = _____

2 Think of a suitable adverb to complete these sentences. Write your adverb.

a The mouse scurried _____ away.

b My sister stormed _____ from the room.

c Gemma thought _____ about the maths problem.

d The star shone _____ in the sky.

e Liam dawdled _____ home.

f Jess _____ scribbled down the phone number.

g My naughty brother behaved _____.

h Dad patted the dog _____.

i We talked _____ in the library.

Making verbs

We can turn some nouns and adjectives into verbs by adding **suffixes** like *ate, en, ify* or *ise*.

With most words you can just add the suffix. If the word already has a suffix, or ends in *e* or *y*, the suffix or final letter must usually be removed before you add the new suffix.

deaf + **en** = deafen

quantity – **ity** = quant

quant + **ify** = quantify

1 Complete these word sums to make new verbs.

a deep + en = _____

b short + en = _____

c standard + ise = _____

d apology + ise = _____

e note + ify = _____

f elastic + ate = _____

g pure + ify = _____

h formal + ise = _____

i wake + en = _____

j medic + ate = _____

2 Add *ate, en, ify* or *ise* to these words to make verbs.

a intense _____

b real _____

c strength _____

d simple _____

e hard _____

f glory _____

g haste _____

h class _____

i serial _____

j weak _____

Irregular verbs

When verbs are used to tell us what a person or thing has already done, most end in *ed*. This is called the past tense.

Present	**Past**
I **look** at the book.	Yesterday I look**ed** at the book.

Some verbs have their own spelling patterns, especially in the past tense. These are known as irregular verbs.

I **keep** rabbits.   I **kept** rabbits.

1 These past tense verbs are wrongly spelt. Write them correctly.

a I hurted my hand.

b Sam putted his toys away.

c Claire runned home.

d Mum bringed my tea.

e I sended you a letter.

f The autumn leaves falled from the trees.

2 Rewrite these sentences, starting with the words in bold. Make sure you spell the past tense verbs correctly. The first one has been done for you.

a I eat my birthday cake.

Yesterday, *I ate my birthday cake.*

b Jamilla buys a comic.

Last week, _____

c Ali draws a picture.

Earlier today, _____

d I am tired.

Last night, _____

e I can swim.

When I was four, _____

f I tell you a secret.

Yesterday, _____

Commas

Commas show us when to **pause** in a sentence.

They are also useful for **breaking up** longer sentences.

Which is your coat, Alex?

Jo, my friend, is eight years old.

Add the missing commas to these sentences.

a After tea we played football.

b Find your trainers Paul.

c Suddenly the lights went out.

d Judy and James from next door came shopping with us.

e My hat which is black matches my scarf.

f Last Tuesday after school I went skating.

Rewrite these sentences, putting the commas in the correct place.

a Tomorrow we, are playing football.

_____

b The ink which, was blue stained, the carpet.

_____

c Eventually Jane, won the game.

_____

d It's, time to go Ali.

_____

e While we were on, holiday we stayed in a hotel.

_____

f At, school in my classroom is a display about, trains.

_____

Powerful verbs

Verbs tell us what a person or thing is **doing**.

The dog **runs**.

Powerful verbs also tell us **how** a person or thing does something. Sometimes they tell us so much, we do not need adverbs.

The dog **runs quickly**.

The dog **sprints**.

1 Sort each verb in the box into its correct group. Then add one more suitable verb of your own to each group.

hobbles argues devours munches shuffles dictates chews declares ambles

walks | **says** | **eats**

a _____ | b _____ | c _____

_____ | _____ | _____

_____ | _____ | _____

_____ | _____ | _____

2 Read the fairytale. Then choose a powerful verb from the box to use instead of the verbs and adverbs in brackets.

Jack and his mother were very poor. One day, Jack's mother (sternly told) _____ him to sell their cow. When he sold it for a handful of beans, Jack's mother (shouted loudly) _____ at him.

Overnight, a magic beanstalk (grew rapidly) _____ up into the clouds. Jack (climbed quickly) _____ to the top and (walked quietly) _____ past the sleeping giant.

As Jack (looked longingly) _____ at some bags of gold, the giant woke up, so he (quickly collected) _____ the gold and (ran away) _____ down the beanstalk.

When he reached the bottom, Jack's mother (cut quickly) _____ away at the beanstalk. The giant (fell heavily) _____ to the ground, and Jack and his mother lived happily ever after.

grabbed

shot

ordered

crashed

yelled

clambered

fled

hacked

gazed

crept

Fronted adverbials

An adverbial is a word or phrase used like an adverb. Adverbs – and adverbials – add information or details to verbs. Adverbials explain **where**, **how** or **when** something happens.

He ate his dinner **after the sun went down.**

verb

adverbial

Fronted adverbials are words and phrases at the **beginning** of a sentence, used to describe the action that follows. Fronted adverbials are usually followed by a comma.

After the sun went down, he ate his dinner.

fronted adverbial

Draw a line to match each fronted adverbial to the most sensible sentence ending.

a Before the sun rose,   he watched the stars.

b In front of the baker's   I'll make lots of festive cakes and biscuits.

c All night long,   he packed his bags.

d Before Christmas,   he waited for his lunch.

e Under a blanket of leaves,   she watched out of the window.

f As quickly as he could,   the hedgehog slept.

g All day,   she ate her breakfast.

Write a fronted adverbial for these sentence endings. Don't forget to put a comma after the fronted adverbial!

a _____ she watched television.

b _____ he waited for his friends.

c _____ the cat meowed.

d _____ the woman giggled.

e _____ the man climbed.

f _____ they wondered.

g _____ she walked away.

Expressing time, place and cause

We can express time, place and cause in a sentence using conjunctions, adverbs and prepositions.

Conjunction	**Adverb**	**Preposition**
I went home **after** school.	**Soon**, I shall go on holiday!	I fell asleep **during** the afternoon.

1 Underline the preposition, adverb or conjunction that expresses time.

a Can you hold this while I eat please?

b I went to the shops before work.

c I went to the park after school.

d It will be home time soon, children.

e I ate popcorn during the film.

2 Write a sentence using each of these words.

a therefore _____

b when _____

c before _____

d soon _____

e during _____

f because _____

g after _____

Tricky plurals

Plural means **more than one** of something.

When you spell plurals, there are rules you have to follow.

Words ending in *f* usually change to *ves* in the plural.

Words ending *ff* just add *s*.

leaf   leaves   cuff   cuffs

1 Underline the correct plural spelling for each word.

a **sniff**   snives   snifs   sniffs

b **half**   halves   halfs   halffs

c **puff**   puves   pufs   puffs

d **cliff**   clifs   clives   cliffs

e **scarf**   scarves   scarfs   scuves

f **scuff**   scufs   scuffs   scuves

g **calf**   calves   calfs   calffs

h **thief**   thiefs   thieves   thiefes

i **yourself**   yourselfs   yourselves   yourselff

j **knife**   knifes   kniffes   knives

2 Write the plural form of these words.

a loaf _____   f wife _____

b self _____   g bluff _____

c sheriff _____   h shelf _____

d cuff _____   i elf _____

e wolf _____   j scoff _____

Choosing words

Choosing the right words for your writing is important.

Some words don't tell us very much.

> We had a **good** time at the party.

Other words are more powerful and tell us much more.

> We had a **fantastic** time at the party.

1 Draw a line to match each word with a more interesting alternative. The first one has been done for you.

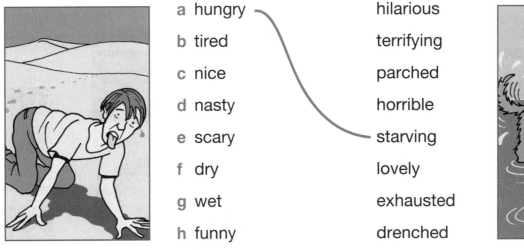

a hungry   hilarious

b tired   terrifying

c nice   parched

d nasty   horrible

e scary   starving

f dry   lovely

g wet   exhausted

h funny   drenched

2 Rewrite these sentences, choosing a better word to replace the words in bold.

a It is **hot** today.

_____

b We **got** some crisps at the shop.

_____

c Kate **made** some biscuits.

_____

d The mouse was **small**.

_____

e We had lunch and **then** we went to the cinema.

_____

Expanded noun phrases

Expanded noun phrases add **interest** to your writing by giving more **information** and **descriptions**. Expansion can happen both before and after the noun.

The monster roared. ⟶ The **scaly** monster, **with long dripping fangs**, roared.

Rewrite these sentences to make them more exciting by using expanded noun phrases.

a The cat jumped.

_____

b The wind blew.

_____

c A rabbit hopped up the lane.

_____

d My mum laughed.

_____

Write a sentence about each of these nouns. Use expanded noun phrases to make things exciting for your reader.

a bat _____

b kitten _____

c ghost _____

d woman _____

e fairy _____

f ship _____

g badger _____

Making adjectives

Adjectives **describe** things or people. We can often make adjectives by adding a suffix to a noun or verb.

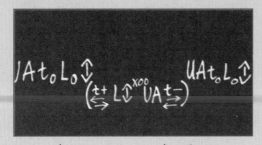

bore + ing = bor**ing**

Words ending in a single *e* drop the *e* when adding *ing* or *able*.

beauty + ful = beauti**ful**

Words ending in *y* change the *y* to *i* when adding *ful* or *able*.

1 Complete these word sums to turn these nouns and verbs into adjectives.

a shock + ing = _____

b wash + able = _____

c trust + worthy = _____

d beauty + ful = _____

e rely + able = _____

f acid + ic = _____

g road + worthy = _____

h amuse + ing = _____

i break + able = _____

j pain + ful = _____

2 Choose *ful* or *able* to make adjectives. Then write the new words.

a wish + _____ = _____

b agree + _____ = _____

c envy + _____ = _____

d hope + _____ = _____

e wonder + _____ = _____

f care + _____ = _____

g adore + _____ = _____

h help + _____ = _____

i value + _____ = _____

j mercy + _____ = _____

More adjectives

Adjectives can help us to compare things or people.

Comparative adjectives compare two things – *bigger, smaller*.

Kate's cat is **bigger** than mine.

Superlative adjectives describe the limit of a quality – *biggest, smallest, most enormous*.

But Mina's cat is the **biggest** of all.

1 Decide whether the adjective in each sentence is comparative or superlative. Then tick the correct box.

	comparative	superlative
a This winter is the coldest on record.	☐	☐
b I live closer to the school than you do.	☐	☐
c I chose the least difficult question.	☐	☐
d My sister is younger than me.	☐	☐
e We saw the longest snake at the zoo.	☐	☐
f Diamonds are more valuable than pearls.	☐	☐
g My house is bigger than yours.	☐	☐
h The theme park was the most exciting place I've ever been.	☐	☐

2 Complete the rows with comparative and superlative adjectives.

	comparative adjectives	superlative adjectives
a	taller	_____
b	_____	narrowest
c	more amazing	_____
d	_____	best
e	older	_____
f	_____	most delicious
g	stranger	_____
h	_____	least interesting

Apostrophes for contraction

If two words are used together a lot, we can sometimes join them together. We do this by taking out some of the letters and putting an apostrophe in their place.

do not → don't

I am → I'm

1 Circle the incorrect contractions.

a **It's Its'** my birthday tomorrow.

b Jake is off school today because **hes he's** ill.

c I **didn't did'nt** do my homework.

d Unless we hurry **wel'l we'll** miss the bus.

e Dad **wo'nt won't** be home until later.

f My brother **wouldn't would'nt** let me watch TV.

g **You're Your're** my best friend.

h **Theyve They've** forgotten their bags.

2 Rewrite these sentences, replacing the bold words with a contraction.

a We **must not** speak in class.

_____

b You can play football after **you have** done your homework.

_____

c He **should not** have eaten so much cake.

_____

d I **cannot** ice skate very well.

_____

e They **could not** find our house.

_____

More apostrophes

Possessive apostrophes are used to tell us when something **belongs** to somebody or something.

With single or collective nouns, the apostrophe usually goes before the s.

With plurals ending in s, the apostrophe usually goes after the s.

The people**'s** shoes   The man**'s** hat

The girls**'** bags

1 Write the missing apostrophes in these phrases.

a the womans bag

b the boys heads

c the childs toy

d the peoples books

e two dogs baskets

f the suns rays

g three footballers boots

h a cats tail

2 Write down the shortened form of each phrase. The first one has been done for you.

a the wings of a bird _____ *a bird's wings* _____

b the pens belonging to the boys _____

c the cat belonging to Kim _____

d the parcels belonging to Sam _____

e the car belonging to my parents _____

f the rattles belonging to the babies _____

g the wallet belonging to my dad _____

h the sweets belonging to the children _____

More suffixes

Sometimes you can add two suffixes to the end of a word.

hope + **ful** + **ly** = hopefully

Sometimes you can add more than one different suffix to a word.

relate + **ion** = relation

relate + **ive** = relative

1 Complete these word sums. Remember the spelling rules for adding suffixes.

a grate + full + ly = _____

b converse + ation + ally = _____

c energy + etic + ally = _____

d photograph + ic + ally = _____

e thank + full + ly = _____

f joy + full + ly = _____

g horrify + ic + ally = _____

h respect + full + ly = _____

2 Pick two different suffixes from the box that can be added to each of these words. The first one has been done for you.

a correct   correct _ion_____   correct _ly_____

b product   product_____   product_____

c construct   construct_____   construct_____

d extreme   extreme_____   extreme_____

e act   act_____   act_____

f real   real_____   real_____

g oppress   oppress_____   oppress_____

h miss   miss_____   miss_____

| ive |
| ly |
| ion |
| ist |

Rhyming patterns

Poets use rhyme in different ways.

Some poems have **alternate rhyming lines**.

Snow *falls*,
Wind *blows*,
Bird *calls*,
Hungry *crows*.

Some lines rhyme in pairs. These are called **rhyming couplets**.

Sunny *days*,
Warm *rays*,
Burning *down*,
Grass *brown*.

Some poems use **no rhyme** at all.

Rain *splashes*,
Wet *feet*,
Dripping *trees*,
Black *puddles*.

Write whether each poem has alternate rhyming lines, rhyming couplets or no rhyme.

a

Black night,

Halloween fright,

Bright moon,

A silver balloon.

This poem has

_____

_____

b

Green trees,

Spring leaves,

Fresh-cut grass,

Crunchy apples.

This poem has

_____

_____

c

Red nose,

Warm scarf,

Rosy glows,

Cosy hearth.

This poem has

_____

_____

Add two lines to each of these poems, making sure you match the rhyming patterns.

a Packed bags,

Luggage tags,

Clutching passport,

Crowded airport,

_____

_____

b Christmas tree,

Gifts below,

Treats for me,

There on show,

_____

_____

Making notes

When we make notes, we only need to write down the **key words**.

1 **Underline the key words in each sentence.**

a Molly and Sam are coming to tea.

b I have gone for lunch, but I will be back at noon.

c My birthday is in December.

d Remember you are playing football on Saturday.

e I have Maths and English homework to do.

f We need to buy some milk and bread.

2 **Write a full sentence for each set of notes.**

a Tea in oven.

_____

b Brownies, Town Hall, 6pm.

_____

c Lucy's party, Friday, buy gift.

_____

d In garden, come round back.

_____

e Mum rang. Running late.

_____

f Car fixed. Please collect.

_____

Prefixes

Prefixes are letter strings added to the beginning of root words to **change** their **meaning**. Here are some examples of prefixes and their meanings.

re back, again

sub under

inter between, among

super above

anti against

auto self, own

---

1 Use the prefixes to help you write the meanings of these words. If you do not know the words, look them up in the dictionary.

a international _____

b remake _____

c automobile _____

d submarine _____

e antidote _____

f replay _____

g superior _____

2 Draw a line to match each prefix to its correct ending.

a re   standard

b sub   place

c inter   biotics

d re   val

e anti   vise

f super   veal

g auto   mobile

Nouns and pronouns

Pronouns help to make writing flow more easily. If you used nouns all of the time, you just repeat yourself.

> The dog walked into the garden. The dog jumped up at the fence and barked, and then the dog lapped up some water.

> The dog walked into the garden. **She** jumped up at the fence and barked, and then **she** lapped up some water.

1 Change the repeated nouns to pronouns. Rewrite the sentences.

a The cat likes milk. The cat drinks it regularly.

_____

b Birds fly into our garden. The birds like our pond.

_____

c A man walked along the beach. The man picked up shells.

_____

d The women were running. The women were keeping fit.

_____

2 Write five sentences using a noun and a pronoun each time.

a _____

b _____

c _____

d _____

e _____

Punctuating speech

When using inverted commas (or speech marks), we have to follow some rules about punctuation and capital letters.

Sometimes we write who is speaking before we write what they say.

Attia said, "Let's go and play!"

Put a comma before the inverted commas. The full stop, question mark or exclamation mark at the end of the sentence goes inside the inverted commas.

Sometimes we write what they say first, then write who is speaking.

"Great, let's go," said Mari.

The first word of a piece of speech always starts with a capital letter.

A comma, question mark or exclamation mark at the end of the speech is used inside the inverted commas.

Look carefully at this piece of writing. Circle the mistakes that have been made with inverted commas, punctuation and capital letters.

"Stop! Thief"! yelled the shopkeeper.

Max asked, "what's the matter?"

"That man stole the money from the till, replied the shopkeeper."

Max asked", Which way did he go?"

The shopkeeper said, "Over the bridge towards the station".

"I'll follow him, and you phone the police", shouted Max.

"You can't escape", panted Max as he ran after the thief.

'You'll never catch me!," replied the thief.

Add inverted commas and punctuation to these sentences.

a Wesley said We're going to Spain on holiday

b Can I have a drink please asked Lola

c Ouch yelled Kira

d Luke asked What time is it

e My big brother shouted Get out

Balanced arguments

A balanced argument needs to include both points of view.

Connectives like *if*, *also*, *then*, *although*, *however* and *on the other hand*, allow us to compare different points of view.

I think swimming is the best sport. Kelly, **on the other hand**, loves tennis.

1 **Underline the connectives in this argument.**

If you spend all your pocket money on sweets, then you will not have any left to buy other things. Also, sweets are bad for your teeth.

On the other hand, if you save some of your pocket money you will be able to buy something you really want. Although it can take a while to save enough, it will be worth it in the end.

2 **Here is an argument about whether children should be allowed to choose when they go to bed. Pick connectives from the box to complete the argument.**

| if   then   on the other hand   however   although   also |

_____ children know how tired they feel, they are too young to understand how much sleep they really need. _____ children are allowed to decide when they go to bed, _____ they may be too tired to concentrate at school. _____, tired children can be very bad-tempered, which could cause arguments at home.

_____, being able to choose their own bedtimes may actually save arguments in the family. Children can always catch up with sleep at the weekends. _____, this would use up a lot of their free time.

Alliteration

Alliteration is when several words next to each other, or very close together, begin with the **same sound**.

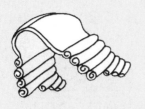

one white wig

bright blue balloon

Using alliteration draws attention to that part of your writing and helps to add rhythm, especially in poetry.

Underline the alliteration in each sentence.

a Daisy danced daintily across the stage.

b Crystal the cat crept cautiously to the door.

c Katie bought a pink patterned purse.

d Philip found frogs in the pond.

e Noble knights never run from battle.

f Gemma tells tall tales.

g Rachel's rabbits wriggled in her arms.

h Nasty gnomes never play fair.

Finish each phrase by adding two more words that start with the same sound.

a beautiful babies _____ _____

b tall trees _____ _____

c honest ogres _____ _____

d sleepy Simon _____ _____

e careful Cara _____ _____

f fat fairies _____ _____

g poor Peter _____ _____

h reckless rhinos _____ _____

The *g* sound spelt *gue* and the *k* sound spelt *que*

English has lots of French words and spellings as part of the language. These spellings can be tricky, so it is a pattern you just have to learn and remember.

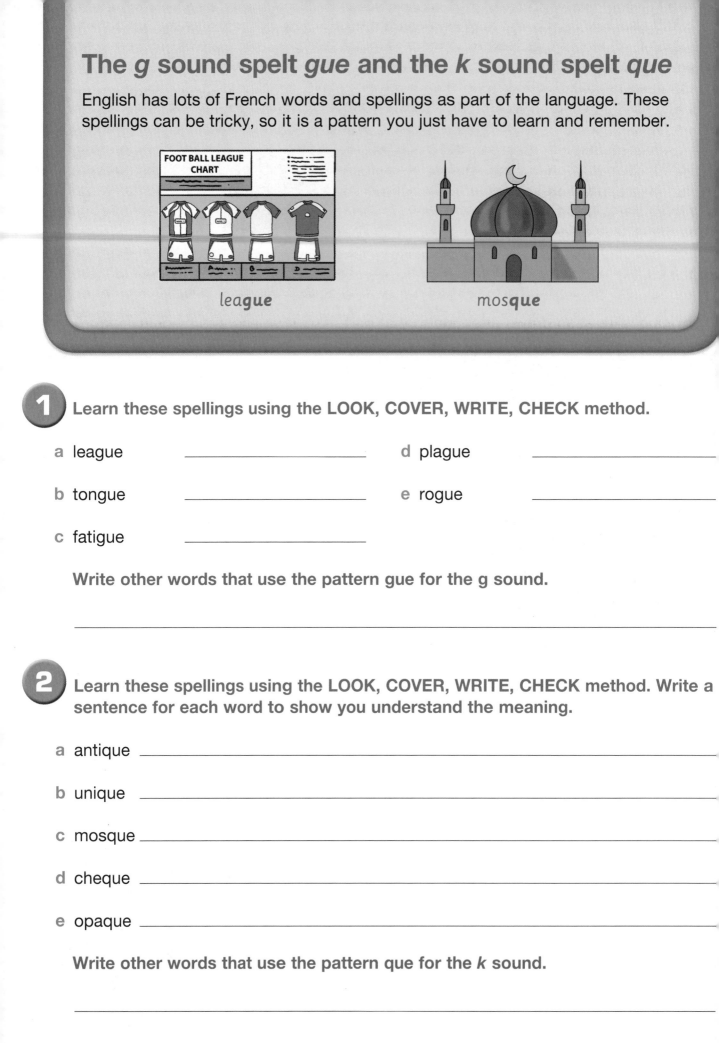

league   mosque

1 Learn these spellings using the LOOK, COVER, WRITE, CHECK method.

a league   _____   d plague   _____

b tongue   _____   e rogue   _____

c fatigue   _____

Write other words that use the pattern gue for the g sound.

_____

2 Learn these spellings using the LOOK, COVER, WRITE, CHECK method. Write a sentence for each word to show you understand the meaning.

a antique _____

b unique _____

c mosque _____

d cheque _____

e opaque _____

Write other words that use the pattern que for the *k* sound.

_____

Its and *it's*

Apostrophes are used to **shorten** and **join** words together.

It **is** my parrot ➡ It**'s** my parrot

They also show when something belongs to someone.

Sian**'s** parrot.

These are called possessive apostrophes. The only exception is *it*, which never has a possessive apostrophe.

The parrot flapped **its** wings.

 Add the apostrophe to *its* in these sentences if it is necessary.

a The cat licked its paws.

b Its my favourite book.

c Its starting to rain.

d The hamster escaped from its cage.

e In the autumn the tree loses its leaves.

f Its easier to roller-skate than ice-skate.

g The dog wagged its tail.

Rewrite these sentences, replacing the words in bold with *its* or *it's*.

a I like popcorn, because **it is** sweet and crunchy.

_____

b **It is** important to take care when you cross the road.

_____

c The bird flapped **the bird's** wings.

_____

d **It is** hot today.

_____

e When **the clock's** battery ran down, the clock stopped working.

_____

f The flower opened **the flower's** petals.

_____

Test 1 The suffix *ous*

Lots of words end in the suffix *ous*. Some words just add *ous* to the root word.

mountain

mountain**ous**

For some *ous* words, *our* in the root word changes to *or*.

vig**our** ➡ vig**or**ous

Add the suffix *ous* to these words. Write the new words.

1. poison_____   _____

2. danger_____   _____

3. mountain_____   _____

4. courage_____   _____

5. outrage_____   _____

6. humour_____   _____

7. glamour_____   _____

Add the suffix *ous* to complete these words.

8. fam_____

9. vari_____

10. tremend_____

11. enorm_____

12. jeal_____

13. seri_____

14. obvi_____

15. curi_____

15
14
13
12
11
10
9
8
7
6
5
4
3
2
1

Colour in your score

Test 2 Which suffix?

These suffixes sound the same.

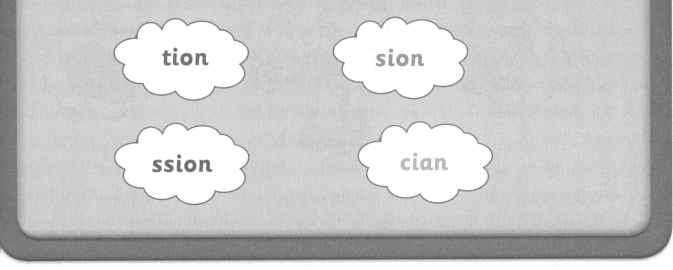

tion

sion

ssion

cian

Use what you know about the suffixes *tion*, *sion*, *ssion* and *cian* to write the correct one to complete each word.

1. musi_____

2. se_____

3. complica_____

4. deci_____

5. mi_____

6. ver_____

7. electri_____

8. adop_____

9. expre_____

10. magi_____

11. addi_____

12. televi_____

13. conclu_____

14. physi_____

15. alloca_____

15
14
13
12
11
10
9
8
7
6
5
4
3
2
1

Colour in your score

Test 3 Verb tenses

Verbs can be written in different **tenses**.

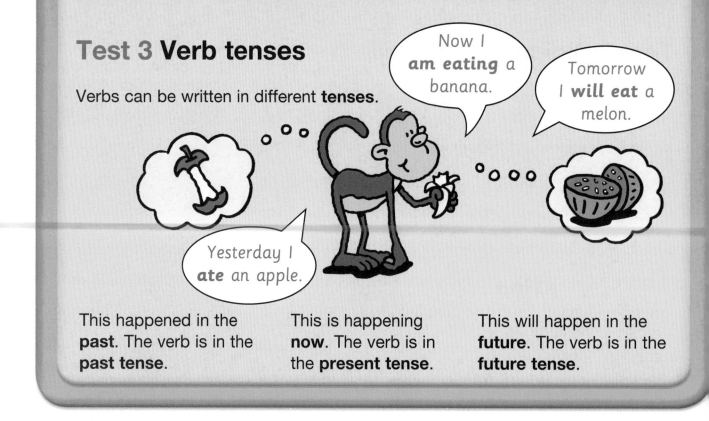

This happened in the **past**. The verb is in the **past tense**.

This is happening **now**. The verb is in the **present tense**.

This will happen in the **future**. The verb is in the **future tense**.

Write if the verb in bold is past, present or future tense.

1. I **will go** out to play after tea. _____

2. We **rode** our bikes. _____

3. I **am swimming** in the sea. _____

4. The girl **dropped** her bag in the mud. _____

5. Tomorrow I **will take** my ruler to school. _____

6. I **like** crisps. _____

7. My mum **gave** me some lunch. _____

8. In the summer I **will fly** on a plane. _____

9. I **sleep** in the top bunk. _____

10. My brother **snores**. _____

11. The car **crashed** into a wall. _____

12. Soon the ambulance **will arrive**. _____

13. Next week I **will leave** for Paris. _____

14. Last year I **went** to Spain. _____

15. I **drew** a picture in my book. _____

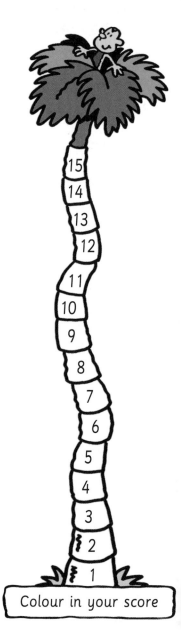

Colour in your score

Test 4 The *k* sound spelt *ch*

The *k* sound spelt *ch* comes from the ancient Greeks. This pattern can be tricky to remember, so it is something that just has to be practised. Build your own **dictionary** – it is always good to use new vocabulary.

Write the meaning of these words. If you do not know the words, look them up in the dictionary.

1. scheme _____

2. chorus _____

3. echo _____

4. chemist _____

5. character _____

6. ache _____

7. school _____

8. chemistry _____

9. chaos _____

10. chameleon _____

11. anchor _____

12. archive _____

13. architect _____

14. chasm _____

15. choir _____

15
14
13
12
11
10
9
8
7
6
5
4
3
2
1

Colour in your score

Test 5 **Suffixes *er* and *or***

A suffix is a **group of letters** we add to the **end of a word**.
A suffix changes the **meaning** of a word or the **job the word does**.

paint (verb)   paint**er** (noun)

Add either the suffix *er* or *or* to make these verbs
into nouns. Take care with the spelling.

1. bake _____

2. visit _____

3. detect _____

4. clean _____

5. build _____

6. edit _____

7. calculate _____

8. dance _____

9. sail _____

10. print _____

11. radiate _____

12. swim _____

13. inspect _____

14. act _____

15. skate _____

Colour in your score

Test 6 Alphabetical order

Many **reference books** are organised in alphabetical order.

light   lion   lizard

These words are organised in alphabetical order according to the **third** letter.

granny   grapes   grass

These words are organised in alphabetical order according to the **fourth** letter.

Order these words according to their third letter.

1. acrobat   act   acorn   _____

2. bacon   baby   badge   _____

3. beach   between   bend   _____

4. daisy   dance   dam   _____

5. door   dock   doughnut   _____

6. fig   fire   film   _____

Order these words according to their fourth letter.

7. climb   cliff   clinic   _____

8. drink   drill   drift   _____

9. earth   early   earn   _____

10. margarine marsh market   _____

11. herring   herb   hero   _____

12. blanket   blast   black   _____

13. brown   brother   broccoli   _____

14. script   scrap   screen   _____

15. through   thrust   threw   _____

Colour in your score

15
14
13
12
11
10
9
8
7
6
5
4
3
2
1

Test 7 Homophones

Homophones are words that **sound alike** but have **different spellings** and **meanings**.

I **heard** a **herd** of elephants coming towards me.

Write the correct word to complete each sentence.

1. The _____ shone in the sky.   (sun/son)

2. I _____ my bike.   (rode/road)

3. He ate the _____ cake.   (hole/whole)

4. I had a _____ of pie.   (peace/piece)

5. I tied a _____ in the string.   (not/knot)

6. You have to _____ an apple.   (peal/peel)

7. I measured my _____.   (waste/waist)

8. The man took the quickest _____.   (route/root)

9. The _____ landed at the airport.   (plane/plain)

10. What _____ do you eat for breakfast?   (cereal/serial)

11. It is wrong to _____.   (steal/steel)

12. Bald men have no _____ on their heads.   (hairs/hares)

13. The ship had two _____.   (sales/sails)

14. The children took _____ bags.   (there/their)

15. It's easy to get _____.   (board/bored)

Colour in your score

15 14 13 12 11 10 9 8 7 6 5 4 3 2 1

Test 8 **Soft** *ch*

The soft *ch* sound that sounds like 'sh' usually means the word has come from the French language and has become part of the English language.

Write the meaning of these words. If you do not know the words, look them up in the dictionary.

1. chef   _____

2. chalet   _____

3. machine   _____

4. brochure   _____

5. chauffeur   _____

6. moustache   _____

7. parachute   _____

8. chaperone   _____

9. chandelier   _____

10. panache   _____

11. quiche   _____

12. crochet   _____

13. chiffon   _____

14. charade   _____

15. ricochet   _____

15
14
13
12
11
10
9
8
7
6
5
4
3
2
1

Colour in your score

Test 9 **Sound spelt sc**

Some spellings show the way the English language has developed over time. The soft *sc* sound comes from the Latin language – used by the ancient Romans.

Learn these spellings, then write a short sentence that contains each word to show you understand the meaning. You can use a dictionary to help you.

1. science _____
2. scene _____
3. discipline _____
4. fascinate _____
5. crescent _____
6. disciple _____
7. scenic _____
8. scientific _____
9. fascination _____
10. disciplined _____
11. scent _____
12. scythe _____
13. fascinator _____
14. scientist _____
15. scenery _____

15
14
13
12
11
10
9
8
7
6
5
4
3
2
1

Colour in your score

40

Test 10 Adverbs

quick – quick**ly**

We can just add *ly* to many adjectives to make adverbs.

merry – merr**ily**

If the word ends in *y*, we change the *y* to *i* and add *ly*.

miserable – miserab**ly**

If the word ends in *le*, we often drop the *le* and add *ly*.

Change these adjectives into adverbs ending in *ly*.

1. sweet _____

2. hungry _____

3. simple _____

4. plain _____

5. proud _____

6. noble _____

7. idle _____

8. glad _____

9. angry _____

10. feeble _____

11. easy _____

12. willing _____

13. lazy _____

14. possible _____

15. steady _____

Colour in your score

41

Test 11 **WOW words**

WOW words make your writing more exciting.

Underline the most exciting and descriptive word in each pair.

1. cold   freezing

2. windy   blustery

3. hot   blistering

4. excruciating   painful

5. wet   drenched

6. parched   dry

7. dirty   filthy

8. old   ancient

9. glittering   shining

10. delighted   pleased

11. nice   wonderful

12. amazing   surprising

13. nasty   wicked

14. beautiful   gorgeous

15. massive   big

Colour in your score

Test 12 **Similes**

A simile is when we **compare** one thing to another, using the words *as* or *like*.

*He was **as** slow **as** a snail.*

Choose the best adjective to complete each simile.

heavy	black	red	quiet	playful	
	sweet	soft	green	smooth	wise
white	fierce	cool	light	slippery	

1. as _____ as honey

2. as _____ as a kitten

3. as _____ as silk

4. as _____ as butter

5. as _____ as a cucumber

6. as _____ as an owl

7. as _____ as beetroot

8. as _____ as a lion

9. as _____ as grass

10. as _____ as an eel

11. as _____ as snow

12. as _____ as lead

13. as _____ as a feather

14. as _____ as a mouse

15. as _____ as coal

Colour in your score

43

Test 13 Handwriting

Neat handwriting is important because it makes your work attractive and easier to read.

Write out these sentences using your best joined-up handwriting. Pay special attention to the spacing of your letters, and their size in relation to one another.

1. I went for a walk in the woods with my granny.

   _____

2. The sun made lovely patterns on the ground.

   _____

3. We saw a beautiful red squirrel in the trees.

   _____

4. Its tail puffed out behind it as it jumped.

   _____

5. There were lots of nuts under the tree.

   _____

6. They had holes gnawed in them by the squirrel.

   _____

7. I picked one up to take home.

   _____

8. I collect things in the woods for my nature table.

   _____

9. I collected red oak leaves and spiky conker cases.

   _____

10. I picked up some sycamore keys and maple seeds.

   _____

Colour in your score

In some words, the soft *i* sound is spelt with a *y*.

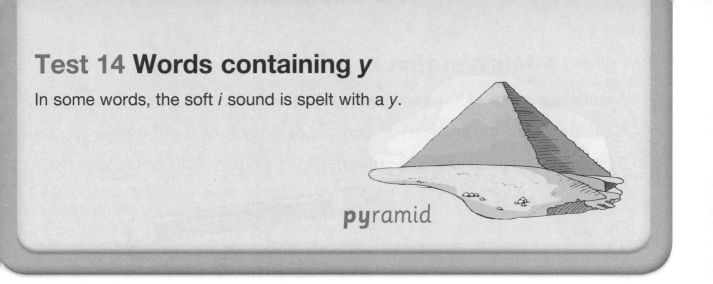

pyramid

Underline the correctly spelt word in each pair.
Cross out the incorrect word.

1. myth   mith

2. histerical   hysterical

3. mistery   mystery

4. cignet   cygnet

5. strict   stryct

6. cristal   crystal

7. pyramid   piramid

8. slypper   slipper

9. gim   gym

10. glisten   glysten

11. trist   tryst

12. pencil   pencyl

13. glympse   glimpse

14. rhithm   rhythm

15. plimsoll   plymsoll

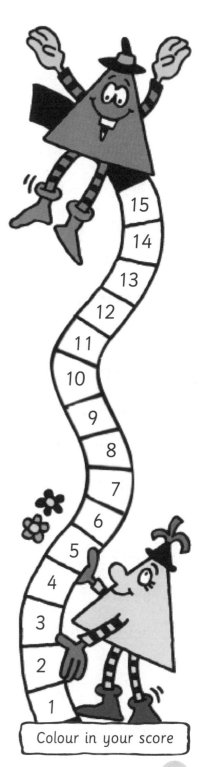

15
14
13
12
11
10
9
8
7
6
5
4
3
2
1

Colour in your score

Test 15 **More suffixes**

A suffix is a **group of letters** we add to the **end** of a word.

A suffix changes the **meaning** of the word or the **job the word does**.

Sometimes you need to change the spelling of the root word before you add the suffix.

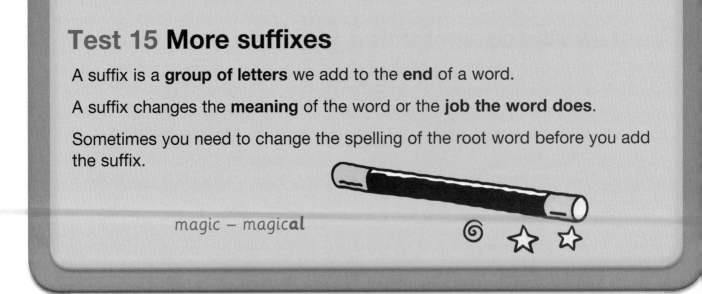

magic – magical

Choose the correct suffix to complete each word.

1. music_____ (al/ous)

2. fashion_____ (able/ible)

3. merry_____ (ment/ous)

4. comic_____ (ment/al)

5. amuse_____ (ous/ment)

6. reverse_____ (able/ible)

7. employ_____ (ment/al)

8. inspect_____ (ion/ment)

9. forgot_____ (able/en)

10. arrange_____ (ion/ment)

11. intense_____ (ate/ive)

12. entertain_____ (ment/al)

13. relate_____ (ion/al)

14. season_____ (al/ise)

15. act_____ (ment/ion)

Colour in your score

46

Test 16 **Dictation**

Dictation is really useful when you want to take notes so you can remember things.

Ask a grown-up to read out these sentences. Listen carefully and write down what you hear on a piece of paper.

1. I went out at night to look at the stars.

2. It was cold outside.

3. I wore a big jumper, a coat and a hat.

4. Mum gave me some gloves to wear.

5. I saw a bat fluttering around the garden.

6. It was chasing the moths flying round the light.

7. The moon was very bright.

8. It lit up the garden.

9. I saw the moon reflecting in the pond.

10. I looked at a star chart, and found some patterns.

11. I managed to find Orion's Belt.

12. Mum showed me the Great Bear.

13. It was getting very late.

14. We came inside and had toast for supper.

15. I'd had a lovely time!

NOTES

15 14 13 12 11 10 9 8 7 6 5 4 3 2 1

Colour in your score

Test 17 **Contractions**

We sometimes **shorten** a word by **leaving out** some letters.
These shortened words are called contractions.
We use an **apostrophe** to show where letters have been left out.

I'm going on holiday.

I'm = I am

Draw a line to match each contraction to its longer form.
The first one has been done for you.

1.	can't	we have
2.	didn't	do not
3.	we've	can not
4.	you'll	it is
5.	that's	did not
6.	don't	I would
7.	doesn't	shall not
8.	you're	does not
9.	shouldn't	they are
10.	we'll	you will
11.	I'd	will not
12.	it's	should not
13.	they're	we will
14.	shan't	that is
15.	won't	you are

Colour in your score

48

Test 18 Commas

Long ago, dinosaurs
roamed the earth.

Commas are used to separate **extra bits** that are **added** to sentences.

The car, a red one, was
parked outside the shop.

Commas help to **break up** longer sentences **into smaller parts**.

Write the missing commas in each of these sentences.

1. That boy the smaller one shouted rude names at me.

2. Don't do that Sam!

3. Pass me my cup of tea please.

4. Feeling rather tired Goldilocks sat down on the chair.

5. Let's go out shall we?

6. Whenever I can I like to go out.

7. Pick up your bag Anna.

8. The dog a spotted Dalmatian escaped from the garden.

9. If I can find one I always buy a comic.

10. Quiet please!

11. No I don't want a sandwich.

12. Whether it's rugby or football I enjoy the game.

13. What's the matter Mrs Shah?

14. Once upon a time there lived an ugly troll.

15. That's very nice thank you.

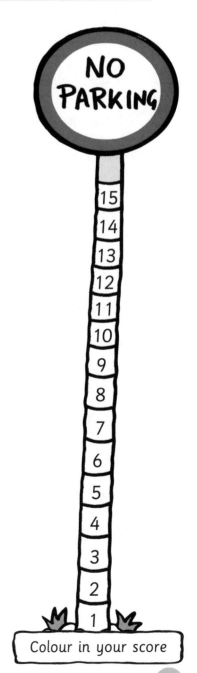

NO PARKING

15
14
13
12
11
10
9
8
7
6
5
4
3
2
1

Colour in your score

Test 19 **Word order**

Sometimes when we **change the order** of words, it **changes the meaning** of the sentence.

The dog chased the postman.   The postman chased the dog.

Rewrite these sentences so they make sense.

1. The sandwich ate a man.   _____

2. The car got into the prince.   _____

3. The crown put on his king.   _____

4. The laugh made us clown.   _____

5. The tree climbed the squirrel.   _____

6. The piano played the teacher.   _____

7. The trunk lifted its elephant.   _____

8. The ball kicked a footballer.   _____

9. Some boots wore children.   _____

10. The runway landed on the plane.   _____

11. An egg fried the girl.   _____

12. The bone picked up the dog.   _____

13. The television is watching Sam.   _____

14. A tunnel went through the train.   _____

15. Stripes have tigers.   _____

Colour in your score

50

Test 20 Apostrophes marking possession

We use an apostrophe to show **ownership** (that something belongs to someone).

When there is **only one** owner, we usually write 's.

When there is **more than one** owner, we usually write s'.

the boy**'s** books
(the books belong to one boy)

the boy**s'** books
(the books belong to more than one boy)

Write the shortened form of each phrase.

1. the bike belongs to the girl   _the girl's bike_

2. the pen belongs to the boy   _____

3. the car belongs to the man   _____

4. the cup belongs to my brother   _____

5. the nuts belong to the squirrels   _____

6. the ship belongs to the sailors   _____

7. the school belongs to the teachers   _____

8. the tie belongs to Sam   _____

9. the bag belongs to Dr Smith   _____

10. the cubs belong to the lion   _____

11. the bananas belong to the monkeys   _____

12. the ball belongs to the footballers   _____

13. the guitar belongs to the singer   _____

14. the barn belongs to the farmer   _____

15. the hose belongs to the fire-fighters   _____

Colour in your score

Test 21 Comprehension (1)

Comprehension is a great way to check you have understood the things you have read.

Read this passage and answer the questions.

I like making models. I collect packaging and scraps, and make them into art! I use old newspaper and PVA glue to make papier-mâché.

My favourite models to make are dragons. I have made a family of different sizes and shapes, and have decorated them with beads, sequins and feathers. The wings are made by carefully cutting shapes from big plastic drinks bottles, and taping them to the bodies of the dragons. I have suspended my flock of dragons from my bedroom ceiling with clear thread, so it looks like they are flying.

1. What does the writer make models from?

   _____

2. What creatures does the writer like making best of all?

   _____

3. What decorations has the writer used?

   _____

4. What are the wings made from?

   _____

5. How does the writer hang her models from the ceiling?

   _____

Colour in your score

Test 22 **Comprehension (2)**

Comprehension tests your reading skills and understanding.

Read this passage and answer the questions.

The hare ran across the moor, its long legs pumping up and down. Everything was starting to grow again, and everything smelled fresh. The hare stopped to sniff the air.

Down the hill, the hare saw two figures. One ran ahead, bounding and jumping. One walked slowly. It was the old man. He watched the hare whenever she ran nearby, but the bounding thing sometimes gave chase. The hare loped down towards trees and brush where she could hide.

The hare settled down cautiously, and the noise of the walkers faded. She dozed as the sun warmed her whiskers.

1. Where does the action of this story take place?

   _____

2. What does the hare see, down the hill?

   _____

3. What creature – 'the bounding thing' – do you think is with the old man?

   _____

4. Where did the hare hide?

   _____

5. Why do you think the hare is 'cautious'?

   _____

Colour in your score

Test 23 The word endings *ssion* and *cian*

The word endings *ssion* and *cian* **sound similar** so spelling these words can be tricky.

For root words ending in *ss* or *mit*, use the suffix *ssion*.

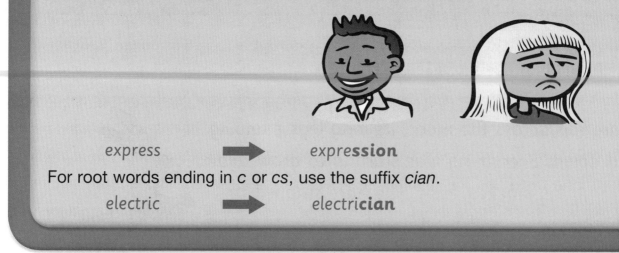

express ➡ expre**ssion**

For root words ending in *c* or *cs*, use the suffix *cian*.

electric ➡ electri**cian**

Add *ssion* or *cian* to complete each word.

1. magi_____

2. mi_____

3. musi_____

4. permi_____

5. politi_____

6. discu_____

7. confe_____

8. techni_____

9. beauti_____

10. aggre_____

11. commi_____

12. mathemati_____

13. profe_____

14. clini_____

15. impre_____

Colour in your score

54

Test 24 **Types of sentences**

There are **four** different types of sentences.

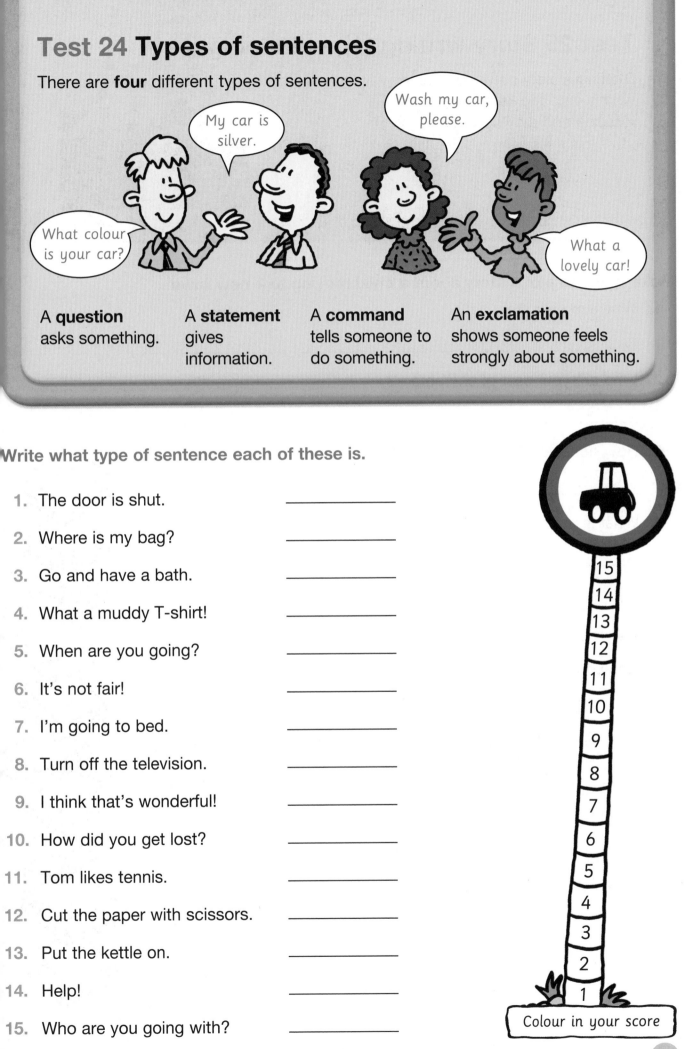

A question
asks something.

A statement
gives
information.

A command
tells someone to
do something.

An exclamation
shows someone feels
strongly about something.

Write what type of sentence each of these is.

1. The door is shut. _____

2. Where is my bag? _____

3. Go and have a bath. _____

4. What a muddy T-shirt! _____

5. When are you going? _____

6. It's not fair! _____

7. I'm going to bed. _____

8. Turn off the television. _____

9. I think that's wonderful! _____

10. How did you get lost? _____

11. Tom likes tennis. _____

12. Cut the paper with scissors. _____

13. Put the kettle on. _____

14. Help! _____

15. Who are you going with? _____

15
14
13
12
11
10
9
8
7
6
5
4
3
2
1

Colour in your score

Test 25 Story writing (1) – planning

Plotting a story before you start
writing helps to keep your story
focused and moving forward.

Make notes to plot a story about a child moving to a new town.

1. Where is your story set?

   _____

2. Who are your cast of characters?

   _____

3. How does your story open? Make it exciting!

   _____

4. What is the main problem that needs to be overcome?

   _____

5. Who will overcome the problem, and how?

   _____

6. Can you identify the theme of your story?

   _____

7. How will you build up excitement or suspense?

   _____

8. Are there any unexpected events or plot twists?

   _____

9. How does the story end?

   _____

10. Can you think of a strong final sentence that will leave the reader
    thinking about your story long after they have finished reading?

    _____

Colour in your score

Test 26 The word endings *tion* and *sion*

The two common word endings *tion* and *sion* sometimes get confused.

invita**tion**

The *tion* at the end of
words sounds like 'shun'.

televi**sion**

The *sion* at the end of
words sounds like 'zhon'.

The ending of each of these words is wrong.
Write each word correctly.

1. conversasion   _____

2. explotion   _____

3. sucsion   _____

4. invation   _____

5. confution   _____

6. preparasion   _____

7. creasion   _____

8. revition   _____

9. competision   _____

10. populasion   _____

11. divition   _____

12. composision   _____

13. conclution   _____

14. inclution   _____

15. fracsion   _____

15
14
13
12
11
10
9
8
7
6
5
4
3
2
1

Colour in your score

Test 27 **The word endings** *able* **and** *ible*

The two common word endings *able* and *ible* sometimes get confused.

comfort + able = comfortable

It is often possible to see the root word when *able* is added.

horror + ible = horrible

It is not always possible to see the root word when *ible* is added.

Choose *able* or *ible* to complete each word.

1. poss_____

2. reason_____

3. terr_____

4. reli_____

5. fashion_____

6. flex_____

7. remark_____

8. suit_____

9. respons_____

10. revers_____

11. sens_____

12. valu_____

13. miser_____

14. favour_____

15. vis_____

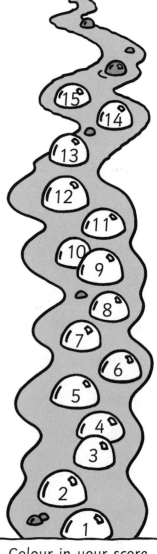

Colour in your score

58

Test 28 **Story writing (2) – characters**

Great characters are so important for any story. Characters are the things people often remember when they think about books they have read.

Use these questions to build a strong 'hero' or protagonist for the story you planned in test 25.

1. Describe your character's physical appearance.

   _____

2. Describe their style of dress.

   _____

3. Is their hair unusually styled or coloured?

   _____

4. What is your character's face like?

   _____

5. How does your character's voice sound?

   _____

6. Does your character have any odd habits?

   _____

7. Does your character have a job?

   _____

8. Does your character have a car?

   _____

9. Does your character have a family or friends?

   _____

10. Does your character have a pet?

   _____

Colour in your score

Test 29 Conjunctions

A conjunction is a **joining** word. It may be used to join two sentences.

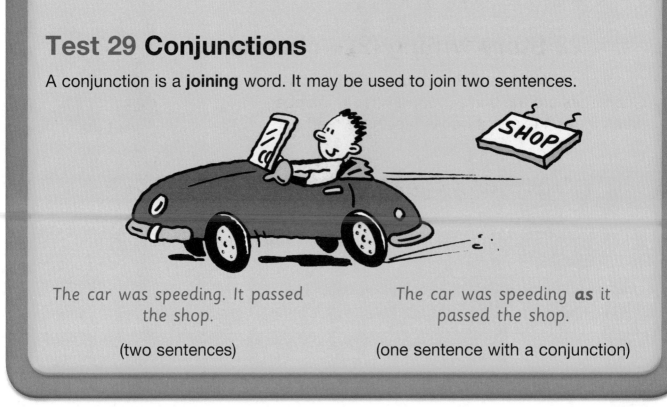

The car was speeding. It passed the shop.

(two sentences)

The car was speeding **as** it passed the shop.

(one sentence with a conjunction)

Find and underline the conjunction in each sentence.

1. It rained heavily but we carried on with the game.

2. The teacher opened the door and the children came in.

3. I went to the shop but it was closed.

4. The children went outside and played in the garden.

5. The monkey will not come unless you give it a banana.

6. He was given the prize because he deserved it.

7. I got lost when I drove through the town.

8. I gave her another sweet as she had eaten the last one.

9. He bought me the present although he couldn't afford it.

10. Do not climb the tree or you might fall.

11. You will not pass the test if you don't try harder.

12. I went indoors when it began raining.

13. The girl will not go to school unless her mother brings her.

14. We started early so we would finish in time for tea.

15. I was nervous as I hadn't seen my uncle for a long time.

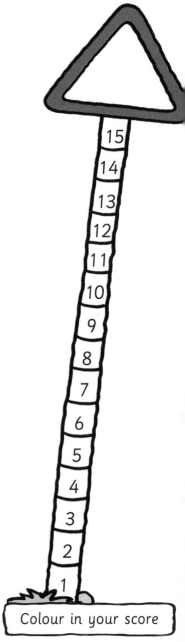

15
14
13
12
11
10
9
8
7
6
5
4
3
2
1

Colour in your score

Test 30 Positive and negative

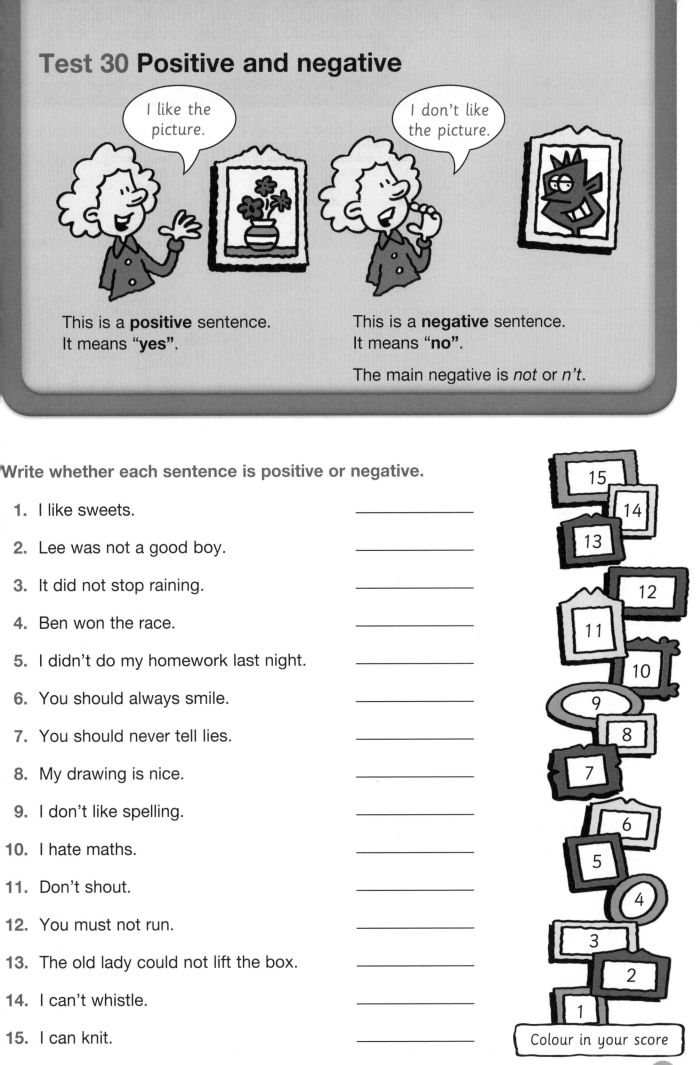

I like the picture.

I don't like the picture.

This is a **positive** sentence.
It means "**yes**".

This is a **negative** sentence.
It means "**no**".

The main negative is *not* or *n't*.

Write whether each sentence is positive or negative.

1. I like sweets. _____

2. Lee was not a good boy. _____

3. It did not stop raining. _____

4. Ben won the race. _____

5. I didn't do my homework last night. _____

6. You should always smile. _____

7. You should never tell lies. _____

8. My drawing is nice. _____

9. I don't like spelling. _____

10. I hate maths. _____

11. Don't shout. _____

12. You must not run. _____

13. The old lady could not lift the box. _____

14. I can't whistle. _____

15. I can knit. _____

15
14
13
12
11
10
9
8
7
6
5
4
3
2
1

Colour in your score

ANSWERS

Page 2
1. Make sure your child can ask questions about schools in the past, and listen carefully to the answers. Encourage your child to think about a variety of topics such as school subjects, food, playtimes and friends.

2. Make sure your child can write an account of the interview that looks at similarities and differences between schools in the past, when the interviewee was at school, and the present day.

Page 3
1. a new
   b whole
   c great
   d their
   e too or to
   f heard
   g see
   h bee
   i four or fore
   j right or rite

2. Any sentences that show your child understands the words given.

Page 4
1. a jumping
   b preferred
   c kicks
   d grabbed
   e gardening
   f saved, saving
   g lifts, lifting

2. a stopped
   b limited
   c carried
   d washes
   e began
   f explores

Page 5
1. a merriment
   b kindness
   c fitness
   d enjoyment
   e laziness
   f membership
   g silliness
   h friendship
   i carelessness
   j happiness

2. a measurement
   b tidiness
   c nastiness
   d employment
   e statement
   f wickedness
   g fellowship
   h apprenticeship
   i replacement
   j championship

Page 6
1. Chat with your child about their favourite film. Make sure they understand the questions, and how much detail to give in their answers.
   a Title of a favourite film.
   b Explanation of why the favourite character is a favourite.
   c An opinion, backed up with reasons, about the most exciting part of the film.
   d An opinion given about the ending, with mention of any problems that have been resolved.

2. a Any 'day out' place mentioned and reason for going (i.e. 'to see the waterfall'; 'to look at sculptures').
   b Description of the journey.
   c Description of the events of the day.
   d Opinion about whether the child would like to repeat the day out.
   e Opinion on whether the day out was good enough to be recommended to a friend.

Page 7
1. a submarine
   b success
   c sudden
   d sugar
   e suitable
   f summer
   g sunny
   h super
   i suspect

2. a hail
   b hair
   c hard
   d hare
   e harp
   f haste
   g hat
   h have

Page 8
1. a completely
   b comically
   c usually
   d sleepily
   e badly
   f totally
   g humbly
   h basically
   i gently

2. Any suitable adverb that makes a sensible sentence.

Page 9
1. a deepen
   b shorten
   c standardise
   d apologise
   e notify
   f elasticate
   g purify
   h formalise
   i waken
   j medicate

2. a intensify
   b realise
   c strengthen
   d simplify
   e harden
   f glorify
   g hasten
   h classify
   i serialise
   j weaken

Page 10
1. a hurt
   b put
   c ran
   d brought
   e sent
   f fell

2. a Yesterday, I ate my birthday cake.
   b Last week, Jamilla bought a comic.
   c Earlier today, Ali drew a picture.
   d Last night, I was tired.
   e When I was four, I could swim.
   f Yesterday, I told you a secret.

Page 11
1. a After tea, we played football.
   b Find your trainers, Paul.
   c Suddenly, the lights went out.
   d Judy and James, from next door, came shopping with us.
   e My hat, which is black, matches my scarf.
   f Last Tuesday, after school, I went skating.

2. a Tomorrow, we are playing football.
   b The ink, which was blue, stained the carpet.
   c Eventually, Jane won the game.
   d It's time to go, Ali.
   e While we were on holiday, we stayed in a hotel.
   f At school, in my classroom, is a display about trains.

Page 12
1. a hobbles b argues c devours
   shuffles dictates munches
   ambles declares chews
   Accept any additional verbs that are suitable.

2. The powerful verbs should appear in the following order in the story: ordered, yelled, shot, clambered, crept, gazed, grabbed, fled, hacked, crashed

Page 13
1. a she ate her breakfast.
   b he waited for his lunch.
   c he watched the stars.
   d I'll make lots of festive cakes and biscuits.
   e the hedgehog slept.
   f he packed his bags.
   g she watched out of the window.

2. Any sensible fronted adverbial followed by a comma.

Page 14
1. a while
   b before
   c after
   d soon
   e during

2. Any sentences which contain the adverb, conjunction or preposition given, and make sense.

Page 15
1. a sniffs
   b halves
   c puffs
   d cliffs
   e scarves
   f scuffs
   g calves
   h thieves
   i yourselves
   j knives

2. a loaves
   b selves
   c sheriffs
   d cuffs
   e wolves
   f wives
   g bluffs
   h shelves
   i elves
   j scoffs

Page 16
1. a starving
   b exhausted
   c lovely
   d horrible
   e terrifying
   f parched
   g drenched
   h hilarious

2. Many answers are possible. Any sensible choice of exciting words for each sentence

Page 17
1. Any more exciting, expanded sentence for each question in the style of the example.
2. Any interesting, descriptive sentences using each of the nouns given.

Page 18
1. a shocking   **f** acidic
   b washable   **g** roadworthy
   c trustworthy   **h** amusing
   d beautiful   **i** breakable
   e reliable   **j** painful

2. a wishful   **f** careful
   b agreeable   **g** adorable
   c enviable   **h** helpful
   d hopeful   **i** valuable
   e wonderful   **j** merciful

Page 19
1. Comparative adjectives are:
b, d, f, g
Superlative adjectives are:
a, c, e, h

2. a tallest   **e** oldest
   b narrower   **f** more delicious
   c most amazing   **g** strangest
   d better   **h** less interesting

Page 20
1. The incorrect forms are:
   a Its'   **e** wo'nt
   b hes   **f** would'nt
   c did'nt   **g** Your're
   d wel'l   **h** Theyve

2. a mustn't   **d** can't
   b you've   **e** couldn't
   c shouldn't

Page 21
1. a the woman's bag
   b the boys' heads
   c the child's toy
   d the people's books
   e two dogs' baskets
   f the sun's rays
   g three footballers' boots
   h a cat's tail

2. a a bird's wings
   b the boys' pens
   c Kim's cat
   d Sam's parcels
   e my parents' car
   f the babies' rattles
   g my dad's wallet
   h the children's sweets

Page 22
1. a gratefully
   b conversationally
   c energetically
   d photographically
   e thankfully
   f joyfully
   g horrifically
   h respectfully

2. a correction, correctly
   b productive, production
   c constructive, construction
   d extremely, extremist
   e active, action
   f really, realist
   g oppressive, oppression
   h missive, mission

Page 23
1. a rhyming couplets
   b no rhyme
   c alternate rhyming lines

2. Any suitable poem endings that use the correct rhyming pattern

Page 24
1. Key words are likely to be:
   a <u>Molly</u> and <u>Sam</u> are <u>coming to tea</u>.
   b I have <u>gone for lunch</u>, but I will be <u>back at noon</u>.
   c <u>My birthday</u> is in <u>December</u>.
   d Remember you are playing <u>football</u> on <u>Saturday</u>.
   e I have <u>Maths</u> and <u>English homework</u> to do.
   f We need to <u>buy</u> some <u>milk</u> and <u>bread</u>.

2. Exact wording may vary.
   a Your tea is in the oven.
   b Brownies is at 6pm at the Town Hall.
   c Buy a gift for Lucy's party on Friday.
   d We are in the garden, come round the back of the house.
   e Your mum rang to say she is running late.
   f The car is fixed, so please come and collect it.

Page 25
1. a existing between nations
   b make again
   c car
   d underwater boat
   e remedy or medicine
   f play again, repeat
   g above/higher/better

2. a replace or reveal
   b substandard
   c interval
   d reveal or replace
   e antibiotics
   f supervise
   g automobile

Page 26
1. a The cat likes milk. She/He/It drinks it regularly.
   b Birds fly into our garden. They like our pond.
   c A man walked along the beach. He picked up shells.
   d The women were running. They were keeping fit.

2. Any sentences which contain a noun and a pronoun, and make sense.

Page 27
1. "Stop! Thief"**(!)** yelled the shopkeeper.
Max asked, "**(W)**hat's the matter?"
"That man stole the money from the till, replied the shopkeeper.**(")**
Max asked "**(,)**Which way did he go?"
The shopkeeper said, "Over the bridge towards the station"**(.)**
"I'll follow him, and you phone the police"**(,)** shouted Max.
"You can't escape"**(,)** panted Max as he ran after the thief.
"You'll never catch me**(!)**" replied the thief.

2. a Wesley said, "We're going to Spain on holiday."
   b "Can I have a drink please?" asked Lola.
   c "Ouch!" yelled Kira.
   d Luke asked, "What time is it?"
   e My big brother shouted, "Get out!"

Page 28
1. <u>If</u> you spend all your pocket money on sweets, <u>then</u> you will not have any left to buy other things. <u>Also</u>, sweets are bad for your teeth. <u>On the other hand</u>, <u>if</u> you save some of your pocket money you will be able to buy something you really want. <u>Although</u> it can take a while to save enough, it will be worth it in the end.

2. Connectives should appear in this order: Although, If, then, Also, On the other hand, However

Page 29
1. a <u>Daisy danced daintily</u> across the stage.
   b <u>Crystal the cat crept cautiously</u> to the door.
   c Katie bought a <u>pink patterned purse</u>.
   d <u>Philip found frogs</u> in the pond.
   e <u>Noble knights never</u> run from battle.
   f Gemma <u>tells tall tales</u>.
   g <u>Rachel's rabbits wriggled</u> in her arms.
   h <u>Nasty gnomes never</u> play fair.

2. Any sensible answers that add words that start with the same sound.

Page 30
1. Can your child spell the words from memory? Any examples of *g* words spelt *gue*.

2. Can your child spell the words from memory? Any sentences which show understanding of the words given and any examples of *k* words spelt *que*.

ANSWERS

Page 31
1. The following sentences need an apostrophe:
   - b It's my favourite book.
   - c It's starting to rain.
   - f It's easier to roller-skate than ice-skate.

2. a I like popcorn, because it's sweet and crunchy.
   - b It's important to take care when you cross the road.
   - c The bird flapped its wings.
   - d It's hot today.
   - e When its battery ran down, the clock stopped working.
   - f The flower opened its petals.

Page 32
1. poisonous
2. dangerous
3. mountainous
4. courageous
5. outrageous
6. humorous
7. glamorous
8. famous
9. various
10. tremendous
11. enormous
12. jealous
13. serious
14. obvious
15. curious

Page 33
The correct suffix is in **bold**.
1. musi**cian**
2. se**ssion**
3. complica**tion**
4. deci**sion**
5. mi**ssion**
6. ver**sion**
7. electri**cian**
8. adop**tion**
9. expre**ssion**
10. magi**cian**
11. addi**tion**
12. televi**sion**
13. conclu**sion**
14. physi**cian**
15. alloca**tion**

Page 34
1. future
2. past
3. present
4. past
5. future
6. present
7. past
8. future
9. present
10. present
11. past
12. future
13. future
14. past
15. past

Page 35
Any definitions which show understanding of the words given, for example:
1. plan, arrangement
2. part of a song repeated after each verse; a group of singers
3. a sound reflected back from a surface to the listener
4. person who carries out chemical research; a shop where medicines are supplied
5. person in a fictional piece of writing; the attributes of a person
6. throbbing pain
7. place where people learn
8. the science of 'matter' – what things are made up of
9. disorder, confusion
10. type of lizard
11. a weight used to hold a ship in place
12. collection of historical documents
13. person who designs buildings
14. deep opening in the earth's surface
15. group of singers

Page 36
1. baker
2. visitor
3. detector
4. cleaner
5. builder
6. editor
7. calculator
8. dancer
9. sailor
10. printer
11. radiator
12. swimmer
13. inspector
14. actor
15. skater

Page 37
1. acorn acrobat act
2. baby bacon badge
3. beach bend between
4. daisy dam dance
5. dock door doughnut
6. fig film fire
7. cliff climb clinic
8. drift drill drink
9. early earn earth
10. margarine market marsh
11. herb hero herring
12. black blanket blast
13. broccoli brother brown
14. scrap screen script
15. threw through thrust

Page 38
1. sun
2. rode
3. whole
4. piece
5. knot
6. peel
7. waist
8. route
9. plane
10. cereal
11. steal
12. hairs
13. sails
14. their
15. bored

Page 39
Any definitions which show understanding of the words given, for example:
1. person who cooks
2. wooden holiday home
3. piece of equipment that makes things
4. booklet with product information
5. a paid driver
6. strip of hair that grows above the lip
7. soft fabric cloth that helps things (including people) fall slowly (e.g. from a plane)
8. person who accompanies someone or a group of people, to keep them safe
9. large light fitting, usually containing crystals
10. flamboyant manner
11. savoury tart made with eggs
12. handicraft using wool and a hooked needle to make things such as blankets
13. type of sheer fabric
14. pretending; a game where words or phrase are acted out
15. something that reboun off a surface

Page 40
Can your child spell the wor from memory? Any sentence which show understanding the words given.

Page 41
1. sweetly
2. hungrily
3. simply
4. plainly
5. proudly
6. nobly
7. idly
8. gladly
9. angrily
10. feebly
11. easily
12. willingly
13. lazily
14. possibly
15. steadily

Page 42
These words should be underlined.
1. freezing
2. blustery
3. blistering
4. excruciating
5. drenched
6. parched
7. filthy
8. ancient
9. glittering
10. delighted
11. wonderful
12. amazing
13. wicked
14. gorgeous
15. massive

Page 43
1. sweet
2. playful
3. smooth
4. soft
5. cool
6. wise
7. red
8. fierce
9. green
10. slippery
11. white
12. heavy
13. light
14. quiet
15. black